Praise for Hanna Golan's

Bless the Children
A Mother's Journal

"So much within the pages of Hanna Golan's *Bless the Children, A Mother's Journal* is rich and dear."

— **Jacquelyn Mitchard,**
New York Times best-selling author of
Twelve Times Blessed, A Theory of Relativity,
The Deep End of the Ocean, and *The Most Wanted.*

———————

"In this delightfully captivating work, Golan masterfully captures the heart-throbbing experiences of childhood's often scary adventures. As parents and adults, we relate to these long gone, yet vivid memories, when reading these short smile-pain evoking accounts."

— **Mike Joseph,** Author of
Middle East: Blueprint for the Final Solution

———————

"Hanna Golan's stories are deceptively simple, drawing you in and then sticking with you to savor. This is a beautiful read that will make your life richer by reminding you of the truths that we all share as adults and as children. Enjoy this lovely book!"

— **Tracy Jones, M.S.,** Author of
The Dessert Diet (www.DessertDiet.com)

"This is so much more than a sentimental journey down memory lane. Hanna Golan's verses read like songs from our past that awaken dreams every mother has – dreams that grace the pages of Bless the Children."

— Rand Chesshir
Abbey Academy of Arts (www.randchesshir.com)

—————

"Hanna Golan's stories in *Bless the Children* not only remind you of your children, but take you back to your own childhood. It's reflective, refreshing and endearing."

— Doreene Hamilton, Author of
Spiritually Speaking... Get Over It!

—————

"The stories within the pages of *Bless the Children, A Mother's Journal* have a charming 19th Century flavor. The rhymes are catchy, the vocabulary is rich without being outlandish, and the grimmest of the stories are reminiscent of Grimm Brothers' tales."

— Michel Phillppart, M.D.
Professor of Pediatric Neurology, UCLA

Hanna Golan

Bless the Children
A Mother's Journal

Flutterby
Publishing

For information, please view webpage:
HannaGolan.com,
or write: hannagolan2000@yahoo.com

FIRST EDITION

Book and Jacket Designed by
Hanna Golan

ISBN: 0-9779723-0-5

Library of Congress Control Number:
2006903325

Printed in the United States of America
on acid-free paper
July 2006

to ...

My Mother
Laja Szydlowski
(7/18/1909 – 7/23/2004)

My Father
Michael David Szydlowski
(10/30/1911 – Healthy Forever)

and ...

Arje Wolf Glowinski
(1861-1941)
Guta Glowinski
(1869-1937)
Szimon Faintuch
(1908-1940)
Guta Faintuch
(1937-1941)

Gerszon Josef Szydlowski
1885-1940)
Fajgl Hana Kaufman Szydlowski
(1890-1940)
Hana Rozenblum Szydlowski
(1910-1941)
Jehoshua Jehuda Szydlowski
(1934-1941)
Chanoch Jakow Szydlowski
(1939-1941)

Dear Readers!

Childhood flutters by on invisible wings — much too fast, much too swiftly. We must capture it all — the joys, the disappointments, and all the wonder of discovery — in our hearts, in our souls, in our memories. The future of the human race depends on it.

This collection of short rhyming stories, *Bless the Children, A Mother's Journal* is, for the most part, a direct extraction from my journal and my way of preserving and treasuring the fleeting moments of my children's and my own earliest years.

Bless the Children, A Mother's Journal contains dramatization for effect and readability, names have been changed to protect the innocent or the seemingly innocent, and some literary liberties have been taken. Otherwise, every story is completely true.

The jacket dressing this book, the illustrations within, and the overall layout are my attempts at creativity. Please forgive their inexpertness and trust that I did my best.

I've arrange my stories in six sections — each roughly depicting a specific topic. You will note that I have embedded some stories in sections which are either irrelevant to the topic of that section or just plain do not belong. These stories recall mishaps which may be emotionally difficult and, at the prompting of some of my critics, I've sandwiched them between stories of a more gentle nature. Additionally, I've segregated stories pertaining to toilet training and such in Section 3, entitled "Nature Calls," with the more squeamish amongst you in mind. Just like any other toilet issues, visit as the urge arises, otherwise, go elsewhere. Remember, each story stands on its own and has no sequential or chronological need to follow or precede any other. Feel free to hop around as often as you wish. I do, however, hope and encourage you to read and reread each one in its own good time.

I want to assure you, dear readers, that none of the injuries discussed in any of my stories within this book were serious, none of the suffering was long lasting, and all the children about whom I've written these stories have long since grown to become well- adjusted and successful adults. Each of them, without a single exception, is now an upstanding member of his or her respective community. I congratulate and applaud them all.

Furthermore, I want to set your minds at ease about the parents in my stories. Just like the children, they survived, matured and are faring very well. Thank you for caring.

Now, allow me to take this opportunity to mention several people who were instrumental in arriving at this finished product, if I may call it that. My husband Mike Joseph, an author of several publications, my first critic while everything was still quite raw, encouraged me to continue with his high ratings. My good friend Anita Pogoda, whom I prompted to be brutally honest and she was, offered some wonderful suggestions. Karen Pogoda, a fine young writer, did a partial editing and pointed out some inconsistencies. Gen Whitt, in spite of her extraordinarily busy schedule, volunteered to do the final editing and further improved the end product. The artistic Rick Chinelli worked his magic and brought the old photographs on the jacket of this book to life.

Several friends contributed stories to my collection as well as some wonderful advice but I will refrain from naming them individually for fear of inadvertently omitting anyone.

Sincere thanks to everyone who took the time, made the effort, invested the energy and offered honest opinions and straightforward criticism. I could never have done it without them.

And lastly, I want to thank you, dear readers, for allowing me to share my memories and my work with you. Thank you from the bottom of my heart.

See you in the subsequent pages and I hope you enjoy viewing them as much as I enjoyed creating them.

Yours very truly,

Hanna Golan
The Author

Contents

1. Little Angels   **1**

    Love.................................... 3

    The Telephone 6

    The Loaded Tray 10

    Swallow-Phobia...................... 12

    The Popsicle.......................... 14

    The Unpeeled Apple 17

    The Sneeze 19

    The Bib................................. 22

    One More............................... 25

    Mommy Baked a Pie................ 27

    Jumping Jack......................... 29

    Morgan Does Not Crawl........... 31

    Cleanly Jim 33

    Where Is My Present?............. 34

    The Mouth 36

    Frannie Is Prissy.................... 39

    Ben Lee 43

    Little Pam 46

    Doctor's Weight...................... 49

    Mommy's New Chore............... 52

    Princess................................ 55

    Won't Smile at Daddy............. 57

    The Drinking Straw................. 59

    Snoozy Susie 63

    The Wink............................... 65

    The Ultrasound...................... 67

Poor Elsie	72
Selective Hearing	74
Mommy's Guardian	76
Shopping Cart	78
Clever Tricks	81
Good Morning World	84
Gary	88
Shelley	89
Jessica-May	93
Windy and Her Umbrella	95

2. Mischief 99

Sporty Marty	101
Mabel McGuire	105
Puppy's Bowl	109
Chocolate Chip Cookies	111
A Day at the Beach	115
Tammy and Her Staff	118
The Birthday Party	121
No More Trikes	126
Daddy's New Radio	128
Muppy and Her Puppy	130
A Bike Race	133
Home from the Zoo	137
Scissors in Hand	140
Lesley's Revenge	142
Trisha Wins Again	147
Wallops on the Hind	151
Head Dive	154
Olivia Flirts	156

Nickie Flipped 159
Randy Swallowed a Coin 163
Sam-the-Ham 166

3. Nature Calls   **171**
Teenage Daughters 173
Donna's Braid 177
Ever-Spreading Puddle 178
Pete Showered Me 183
Rancid Stream 186
Heidi and Paige 188
Inquisitive Vicki 189
Little Helper 191
Our Roy 194
Infant Michael 197
Monkey-See-Monkey-Do 200
Toilet Training 202
Upside-Down Child 205
The Potty 209
Standing Up 211
Don't Pee in My Pool 213
Mia 216
Linda 218
Soiled Diapers 221
Has a Bark but No Bite 225
Very Deep Cup 228

4. At School   **231**
Rambling Eyes 233
The New Thermos 235

Where Is Shawn's Shoe 240
Maya 243
New Girl at School 247
The Smiths 251
Angry at Teacher 255
Teacher Says Otherwise 257
The Math Test 260
Out the Window 264
The Waving Hand 267
Puppy Love 269
Second Floor Window 271
The Hall Monitor 273
The Board Monitor 275
Teacher's Pet 277
Parents Have Forgotten 279
A Touch of Excitement 281
Parent-Teacher Night 283
Substitute Teacher 286
The School Janitor 289
School Was Discovered 292
Isabel 295
Handful of Worms 298
The Broken Wrist 301
Francy in Kindergarten 306

5. Wee Wisdom   **309**
Trumpets and Clarinets 311
All in Knots 313
Chocolate Is Too Cold 316
Raisins in the Bottle 320

Eating Is a Bore 323
How to Hold the Bottle 326
Christie 328
Buy Some Money 331
Baby Is Eating Mommy 334
Star-Studded Skies 336
Erica...................................... 339
Baby on a Park Bench............. 341
Afraid to Sleep 344
Sharing Dreams...................... 346
The Looking Glass................... 348
Cousin Amos 352
Milk Is White 355
Pictures in the Night 358
Eyeglasses 361
They Get Injected 363
A Peculiar Fellow 366
Heather 368
Sweaters in the Heat 370
Small World 372
What Is Rain? 374
Rickie and Mickie................... 375
Flooded Basement................... 378
The Injection.......................... 381
The Funny Bone 384
Defective Baby 387
Mommy's Flower Garden......... 389
Battle Scars 391
Baby Discovers Toes 394

6. Mom Wisdom   **397**

Not Fair 399
Why? 403
Siblings Fight 405
My Dad Is Better 406
Our Child 408
I Don't Know 411
Three Is a Crowd 413
Hug Your Children 415
Horseback Riding 417
To Err Is Human 421
The Bogeyman 423
Your Child Is Crying 426
A Bundle of Peril 428
Age Discrimination 431
Minnie Versus Mickey 434
No, No, No! 437
I Was Raised This Way 439
It Does Not! 441
The Terrible Threes 443
Wrong Tree 446
Freddy's Arm 448
A Fallen Leaf 451
Communication 453
Zipper Chin 456
Boys and Girls 459
The Teenager 461
Guardians of Peace 465
Suffering Teens 467
Don't Toy with Your Food 469

Love

In a public playground, on a see-saw,
Two young children played with no
    wish to withdraw.
He wore blue jeans and a white shirt,
She a ruffled blouse and a pink skirt.

Playing and giggling and having fun,
They'd skip, jump and sometimes run.
All went superbly until Mother called
    her to leave,
His Father pulled him away gently
    by a sleeve.

Feeling no resentment as to Mother
    she went,
He wasn't angry for being home sent.
Such was the conclusion of a wonderful
    day,
Both knew that tomorrow
    they'll once again play.

He and she met again in the morrows,
Joyfully contented as lighthearted
    sparrows.
Down slides they went one after the
    other,
With other kids they wouldn't even
    bother.

Such was their courtship among slides
    and swings,
A blossoming friendship from hoops
    to rings.
He and she loved one another as only
    three-year-olds can do,
They looked so cute together, those two.

4   Bless the Children

One day she took his hand in hers
    and left it there to linger,
Stroking it with a concerned finger.
Checking the tip which rubbed the
    palm of her befriended,
Whilst the other hand he too extended.

Her intention was pure and not wishing
    to scoff,
She was rubbing to check if the color
    would come off.
He was brown skinned and with curly
    dark hair,
She blond and blue eyed and skin
    very fair.

The Telephone

Ernie's always had an abundance of
  toys,
Balls and stuffed animals he greatly
  enjoys.
He possesses tin soldiers and trucks,
And for the bathtub, yellow rubber
  ducks.

Among his favorites without a doubt,
Is the red telephone, I found out.
He feels mature when holding it to
  his ear,
Earnestly chatting though response he
  doesn't hear.

"To speak on the phone." One day
    Ernie insisted,
"Not the red one, but Mom's and
    Dad's," he persisted.
So, Dad dialed a number to connect
    with Ernie's Auntie,
Receiver to his ear, Ernie held firm
    though dainty.

His eyes clearly declared, "I'm a big
    boy now!"
But when the receiver spoke he jumped,
    and how.
This was so different from his own
    little red phone,
This actually spoke following a very
    strange tone.

Poor Ernie was baffled at such an
    occurrence,
And distrusted Dad's reassurance.
The voice sounded unfamiliar,
But Dad insisted, "It's Auntie Tilliar."

"Speak to your auntie," Dad urged
    repeatedly.
But Ernie suspected that Dad is teasing
    him deliberately.
Distrustful and wary, Ernie removed
    the receiver,
Intending to get the best of his deceiver.

Checking and inspecting from each
  possible angle,
The cord around his arm became
  a messy tangle.
The receiver was still calling Ernie's
  name,
This was some strangely unfamiliar
  game.

The Loaded Tray

Hip, hip, hurray! Hip, hip hurray!
Mom is bringing out a large loaded
    tray.

The tray is filled with variety of
    yummies,
We'll all eat and fill our tummies.

Sandwiches, chips and dips of different
    sorts,
My friends and I are the best of
    consorts.

They gather to celebrate a special
    occasion,
All bestowing gifts which I accept with
    elation.

Today I'm completing four years of my
    life,
Mostly joyous but some marred with
    strife.

I deserve respect for weathering it all,
And look! I grew so very tall.

Swallow-Phobia

Cindy was afraid to swallow, or so it
   seemed at every meal,
Endlessly chewing even liquids and
   mushy oatmeal.
She gladly opened wide to welcome
   the food,
But in her mouth it would stay for good.

From one cheek to another the mass
   shifted,
Munching teeth repetitively lifted.
Hard working tongue on the attack,
Bright lips against one another smack.

I begged and beseeched her, "Cindy,
   please swallow,"
But more mastication was all that
   would follow.
Frustrated, I left Cindy alone at the
   table,
To continue the feeding I was unable.

Ten minutes later, she was still
    working hard,
Wouldn't swallow nor discard.
There was nothing wrong with her
    appetite,
It was a peculiar phobia to swallow after
    a bite.

Putting aside my anxiety and worry,
Logical thinking took over in a hurry.
In spite of it all, Cindy was growing,
So, into her body nutrition must be
    flowing.

While chewing between each cheek,
Some food must penetrate in a slow
    leak.
Tongue, teeth and lips continued their
    chore,
Occasionally stopped to admit some
    more.

The Popsicle

Have you ever seen my Cheryl eat
    a popsicle?
That, I assure you, is quite a spectacle.
It's an elaborate process, freeing
    popsicle of its wrapping,
But she somehow manages to strip it
    of all trapping.

Now comes the fun part and lip
    smacking delicacy,
I'll do my best to relay it with detailed
    accuracy.
Having the sweet by its exposed stick,
Cheryl first must decide which end to
    lick.

Holding it cautiously so it won't drop,
Inevitably, Cheryl starts at the top.
The weather is hot and the chilled
    dessert is thawing,
Streaks of sticky stuff down her fingers
    are drawing.

A gooey stream starts its sugary track,
Ugh! Cheryl is a terrible wrack.
The current is ever increasing,
And its flow is never ceasing.

Cheryl tries to speed up her licking,
Tongue is now reaching for spots that
    are sticking.
From arm to elbow
    Cheryl savors,
It's sweet and the
    flavor she favors.

Cheryl finally realizes her plight,
So at the melting popsicle she goes
    with might.
The other hand is summoned for
    assistance,
Because dissolving continues with
    persistence.

By now, Cheryl is holding a barren
    cane,
Without its coating it is rendered
    mundane.
Her forehead is smudged for she
    soothed an itch,
And her clothing hasn't been spared,
    not a stitch.

The Unpeeled Apple

Toothless mouth, tiny but delightful,
Surprisingly mighty and powerful.
It coos and it babbles,
Bibfuls of saliva dribbles.

Inserting objects large and small,
Sucking and gnawing at them all.
The most amazing of all its flairs,
Becomes obvious when to bite hard
    it dares.

Clamped gums can cause a great deal
  of pain,
Efforts to release may prove in vain.
I've seen Andy, with tiny hands like
  paws,
Zestfully introducing an apple between
  robust jaws.

Seemingly useless, Andy's gums are
  quite ample,
To easily chew a whole unpeeled apple.
I don't possess answers to such an
  incredible wonder,
Andy does well toothless, why then
  should he need teeth? I ponder!

The Sneeze

Infant Seki is hungry and shrieking for
    her bottle,
With a feeding Mommy tries her crying
    to throttle.
The bottle contains delectables and the
    best of ingredient,
Such as doctors recommend and
    Mommy is obedient.

In the past, Seki liked this foodstuff,
But today she's all in a disdainful huff.
Refusing the bottle which Mommy
    introduces,
Though Mommy coaxes, persuades
    and induces.

After a long struggle of wills,
Seki's whimpering stills.
The nipple is finally tackled,
Rubbery tip greedily suckled.

Appeased, Mommy continues the task,
Facial grimace alters to a happy mask.
Infant Seki is sucking with gusto and
  zeal,
This feeding is no longer a difficult
  ordeal.

Minutes go by and all appears to be
  swell,
Seki and Mommy are getting on quite
  well.
Mommy's worries are for now erased,
If only she'd been forewarned and
  securely braced.

Something suddenly tickles Seki's
    nose,
And her velvety skin turns to rose.
Nostrils twitch left and right,
Little body shivers and stiffens tight.

A fountain of spray ejects from wide
    open mouth,
Rejected bottle flies north and lands
    south.
Splattered, Mommy remains in an
    unnatural freeze,
Failing to realize that this is a mere
    sneeze.

The Bib

I have yet another story for you,
Be patient and I'll tell it with no further
    ado.

About a tiny apron is my tale,
Around baby's neck it was meant
    to hail.

It is referred to as Bib, I know not why,
And it's there to protect baby's chest
    and keep it dry.

As Mommy tied Bib around Eric's neck,
He pulled it off without a moment's
    check.

Once again, Bib and Eric were
  connected,
But with Eric's quick jerk Bib was
  rejected.

This battle for power went on for a
  while,
Mommy fastening, Eric dispatching Bib
  into exile.

Mommy endlessly fetched after every
  toss,
It was easy to tell who here was the
  boss.

Bib was thrown and flung and ripped
  apart,
Crumbled and crushed right through
  its heart.

Soon Bib's strings were lost and gone,
It was rendered expired and done.

Realizing additional efforts in vain,
Mommy resolved to stop Bib's pain.

Exhausted, she simply gave up trying,
Tattered on the floor Bib was left lying.

One More

Sitting at a bus stop one bright day,
In public transportation I wished to
    partake.
Along came a mother and child of
    three or four, I couldn't say,
A trip on the bus they too wanted
    to take.

Into my purse I dug and extracted,
A bag of colorful sweets.
The child was promptly attracted,
To my chocolaty treats.

He helped himself and with a smile
   I was compensated,
Mom silently looked on.
Noisily he sucked on the candy,
   contented,
While observing Mom wasn't done.

She sternly looked down,
"Have you forgotten what to say?"
"Yes Mom," the child replied with
   a frown,
And embarrassed looked my way.

Suddenly his face brightened,
"May I have one more?"
His small fist untightened,
Anticipating to receive sweets
   as before.

Mommy Baked a Pie

Honey has been watching Mommy
    bake a pie,
Warm and candied, its appearance
    won't belie.

Honey thought, contemplated and
    reflected,
"If I were a pie I'd be quite perfected."

"I'd be sugary and spicy and overly
    tasty,
I'd be loved for being sweet and pasty."

"I'd be nice and warm and toasty,
Creamy and fruity and roasty."

"Mommy would gently caress and
    cuddle,
While forgiving my every muddle."

So, into the oven Honey mounted,
Potential hazards were discounted.

Oh Honey! Oh Honey! Take my advice,
Unbaked and unsweetened you'll
    quite suffice.

No pie in the world could be quite as
    sweet,
You are much better than any sugary
    treat.

Jumping Jack

Jumping Jack is an appropriate name
    for such a boy as he,
Where you place him he won't for very
    long be.
Jumping up in an instant from where
    you set him,
Chances that he'll tarry are rather slim.

I don't really know what makes
    Jumping Jack jump,
But I'm certain that you'll never see
    him slump.
He's a chubby rounded baby boy,
Jumping Jack is a marvelous living toy.

He's consistent and predictably reliable,
The fact that he'll continue jumping is
  undeniable.
If you don't believe or trust what I say,
You're welcome to try it any day.

Choose a site in which to place Jumping
  Jack,
Lay him down on his tummy or on his
  back.
In a few seconds, I can safely guarantee,
Upright and erect Jumping Jack will be.

Morgan Does Not Crawl

Morgan is already seven months old,
But he still can't crawl, I'm told.
Unlike many young ones of similar age,
Awkward squirming is his mode of
    voyage.

To slither on his belly poor Morgan
    must resort,
While crawling for his peers is now a
    proficient sport.
It seems that seven-month-old crawlers
    in this great big creation,
Swiftly move about while Morgan drags
    in painstaking progression.

Morgan hasn't learned to lift himself
    off the ground,
Advancing on hands and knees in
    a motion onward bound.
Comically, hauling the full length of
    his physique,
Using elbows as propellers is an
    inefficient technique.

Cleanly Jim

Jim is an unusually cleanly imp,
At washing I've never seen him skimp.

Always attempting to keep neat and
   trim,
Near a puddle one will never see my
   Jim.

He carried his hygiene too far,
   I perceive,
When wiping his shoes with a white
   shirt sleeve.

Where Is My Present?

It's Sophie's fifth birthday and she
    feels so grown,
She's filled with joy for reasons well
    known.
There'll be a party this very afternoon,
Friends will begin arriving soon.

Two by three or four, guests come
   to partake,
Gladly wishing to share Sophie's
   birthday cake.
What Sophie looks forward to most
   of all,
Is unwrapping gifts, now lining up
   against the wall.

Some of the younger callers came
   empty handed,
"Where is my present?" Sophie
   demanded.
After all, why have a party if you
   can't compile,
A heap of presents which to open
   requires a long while?

The Mouth

Articles will be inserted into most
 unlikely places,
Such is done by children of all nations
 and races.
When finding an object of the right size,
Into the nearest cavity a child implants
 whether appropriate or otherwise.

And what is most convenient and
 always at arm's reach?
For which hollows a child doesn't have
 far to search?
Which are ever handy and always
 willing to accept?
Where are the holes which for burial
 of tiny items are so adept?

Yes, you have guessed it, effortlessly
    with ease,
These are bodily craters, if you please.
Marbles and teddy bear eyes will all be
    hidden,
Tucked into ears but not ridden.

There is no better place to conceal
    buttons, I suppose,
Than in the tiny navel or the freckled
    nose.
When tiring of the left nostril, the right
    is just as willing,
If in need of extra space, simultaneously
    both are receiving.

The best of all hiding places is the
    mouth, for all it can retain,
Receiving deposits, again and again
    and again.
Unlike the other crevices of the child's
    body,
The mouth expands greatly for more
    items to embody.

There are several important points
    which I must however make,
The mouth has a tendency to swallow
    so beware what you take.
It also obnoxiously wets all that it
    touches with a tongue, oh so sloppy,
And if it wants it can break things with
    its teeth, chop, choppy.

Frannie Is Prissy

Frannie has always been prim and
    prissy,
I don't know where she got it 'cause
    I'm such a sissy.
She must dress just so,
An improper attire is her biggest foe.

Frocks must fit perfectly around her
    trim little figure,
Frannie refuses shorts for being too
    meager.
Slacks are inappropriate for little
    ladies of stature,
Thus skirts and dresses are
    her permanent fixture.

At hairdos Frannie spends time to no
measure,
A pin or beret is an unmistakable
treasure.
Belts, purses, scarves and other such
accessories,
Are Frannie's bare essential necessities.

But now Frannie has matured into
bigger things,
She must have bracelets and bejeweled
rings.
Mom has all those wonders and many
more,
Makeup and lotions, fresh from the
store.

Frannie has outgrown her cute little
   dresses,
Will no longer tolerate her hair in long
   tresses.
Mom's evening gowns Frannie prefers
   to wear,
She dons them carefully to avoid a tear.

Her hair is adorned by Mom's velvety
   hat,
With rouge, young cheeks are
   smeared at.
Long earrings and a necklace or two,
All oversized but Frannie makes
   them do.

The best part of dressing up are Mom's
    high heels,
Making her wobble and glide as if they
    had wheels.
Both small feet can fit one shoe,
Looking grown–up is what she wants
    most to do.

Ben Lee

This universe is abundant with
    wondrous secrets,
Blessed with brilliant sounds of
    symphonies and cabarets.
Multitude of brightly colored flowers,
    birds and butterflies,
Hordes of horses and cats and fish
    and dragonflies.

An opulence of creatures such as
    dogs, elephants and sheep,
Fields of grass and tall trees under
    which one likes to sleep.
Creation is also generous to human
    faces,
For they come in many shapes, colors,
    sizes and races.

Angela is a delving youngster,
An experimenting little tester.
She pondered one day about Ben Lee,
"How are his eyes able to see?"

Angela didn't intend to appear the
    prankster,
But tact in her youth she didn't yet
    master.
Two fingers stretched her eyes to
    narrow slits,
Now satisfied that Ben Lee's appearance
    she fits.

Though trying with all her might,
Angela was getting a blurry sight.
Creation dealt Ben Lee eyes which
    are bogus,
For she found them impossible to
    focus.

Nature cheated poor Ben Lee and his
    kin,
What has befallen them is no doubt
    a sin.
This angered Angela greatly,
As she stared at Ben Lee, irately.

In spite of it all, Ben Lee seems to have
    adjusted,
"He must be seeing things," Angela
    after all trusted.
He seems to be happy with this cosmic
    plot,
Angela admires him for that a whole lot.

Little Pam

Daddy and his little girl, Pam,
His kitten and beloved lamb.
He loves playing rough,
Knowing that little Pam is tough.

Daddy tackles Pam to the floor,
She giggles and pleads for more.
He hoists her up high in the air,
She's got the natural flair.

Daddy tosses Pam over his
   shoulder like a potato sack,
Her legs dangle in front while her
   head rebounds off his back.
He hops and skips with Pam thus
   prone,
She titters and twitters while her
   body is thrown.

They're both having fun, Pam and
    Daddy, en masse,
Neither anticipates that which is
    about to pass.
Daddy's rapid movements cause
    Pam's head to jolt,
What ensues is serious enough
    for them both to halt.

Involuntarily, Pam's sharp teeth
    bite at her own tongue,
Causing her to scream at the top
    of her lung.
Daddy is overcome with dreadful
    fear,
While Pam continues
    shrieking in his ear.

Daddy peels Pam off his shoulder
    very gently,
As she continues to cry greatly.
The blood is oozing profusely,
Daddy realizes that he's behaved
    obtusely.

Tongue is injured but not too badly,
Remorsefully, Daddy looks at Pam
    sadly.
Bleeding stops as she perches
    on his lap,
And soon forgets the entire mishap.

Doctor's Weight

*What's good for the goose is good for
    the gander,*
That philosophy Astrid will never
    surrender.
What grown-ups can say and do,
Astrid will too.

One day a woman asked Astrid her age
    and name,
Astrid wanted to know of the woman
    the same.
Exchanging of names was fine and
    pleasing,
But the question of age was perceived
    rudely teasing.

Another affair caused me to redden
    from face down to neck,
It occurred when taking Astrid to the
    doctor for her annual check.
A giant, triple chinned and potbellied
    doctor entered with a smile,
Examining, he probed Astrid for quite
    a while.

Doctor prescribed a laboratory test,
Astrid's weight he also wished to arrest.
Barefooted, on the scale Astrid stood
    sedate,
While doctor leaned close to read her
    weight.

As he logged Astrid's poundage in
    a chart,
She looked up at his face and asked
    with a smart.
"Doctor, how much do you weigh?"
Needless to say, she spoiled my
    whole day.

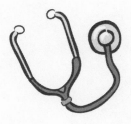

Mommy's New Chore

Long silky brown hairs,
Waist length tresses Melissa wears.
At times a single braid is woven from
    behind,
At others, two on either side of the
    face are assigned.

Melissa isn't in control of her own
    hair yet,
It's difficult to manage especially
    when wet.
So her hair is one of Mom's many
    chores,
Mom finds it pleasurable and a task
    she adores.

Melissa scratched at her skull one
 day after school,
Clawing at hair which now looked
 like tangled wool.
To survey Melissa's hair, Mom
 approached,
Discerning that a new assignment
 must at once be broached.

What Melissa has contracted,
Are lice which must immediately be
 extracted.
Her afflicted filaments will be treated
 with a chemical,
A powerful substance, diabolically
 inimical.

With a fine-toothed comb Melissa's mop
    must be gone over,
Each and every strand Mom must
    uncover.
Not one tiny louse may remain,
Mom will work long hours purification
    to attain.

Princess

To the kingdom of Home and Fortress,
Was born a lovely Princess.

Princess was as plump as a dumpling,
Good disposition never crumpling.

Months passed and Princess grew,
In the kingdom she's no longer new.

On a highchair, a cushioned throne,
Princess sits bigger but not yet grown.

Crossing her legs in Buddha style,
Princess presides over her serene isle.

Content and appeased she sits in her
    realm,
Pleasure and cheer are her
    unquestionable helm.

Her face is charged with smiles,
Radiating tranquility and peace for
    miles.

Round belly, butter ball,
Parents gaze proudly, feeling ten
    feet tall.

Won't Smile at Daddy

Daddy's little angel, more precious
    than words can relate,
Causing his heart and soul with
    adoration to pulsate.

What can be worth more than this
    bundle of joy?
What can be more miraculous than
    this wonderful toy?

His every wish was answered when
    this cherub was born,
Gratified and in reverence, Daddy
    could now blow his own horn.

One ache, however, Daddy must
    tolerate,
Severe enough to cause his blood
    pressure to elevate.

This child, his jewel, must have been
    bewitched,
Sighting a mere neighbor, her smiling
    mouth twitched.

Jealous, Daddy tried and tried,
But a smile his gem had not supplied.

Daddy was hurt and even filled with
    anger, I'll wager,
Because the love of his life would
    smile only for a stranger.

The Drinking Straw

Dad behind the wheel, Mom beside
  him,
Penny in the back, with enthusiasm
  they brim.
The drive to the park isn't very long,
Contented, they intone a cheerful
  song.

Anticipating heat and inevitable
  thirst,
Mom prepared food but cold drinks
  were packed first.
They eat and drink and have
  a wonderful time,
Appreciating these hours of
  harmony as prime.

The three play ball and a Frisbee
    is hurled,
For resting, plaid blankets are
    unfurled.
None remembers when last having
    so much fun,
Under a shady tree or in the bright
    warm sun.

As all good things must end so
    does this outing,
The prospect finds them sadly
    pouting.
Into an awaiting car belongings
    are orchestrated,
With a cold soda Penny is
    compensated.

She drinks it all in a hurry,
Finishing in a scurry.
The empty can is forsaken,
Into the mouth straw is once
   again taken.

What is noted with apprehensive
   awe,
Is Penny's chewing at the straw.
Straw in mouth while sitting in
   the rear,
Causes Mom and Dad endless fear.

As sooner as they request that straw
   be removed,
Their premonition is sadly proved.
Dad slams on his brakes to avoid
   a crash,
Down Penny's throat straw
   glides in a flash.

The infamous straw stops half
  in and half out,
But poor Penny can't even shout.
She is obviously in pain,
While Mom attempts to stop the
  bleeding in vain.

They rush Penny to the hospital
  with one thought in mind,
To reach a doctor that will get them
  out of this bind.
Thankfully, the incident is less
  serious than it appeared,
The injury is superficial because
  no vitals are speared.

Snoozy Susie

Snoozy Susie, my cuddly bunny,
Asleep in a crib face down.
While sticking up her fanny,
Little hands tangled in her gown.

Head on the pillow,
One cheek resting right or left.
The one visible all aglow,
The other hidden from the draft.

Little angel in a slumber,
What are you viewing in your dreams?
I pray life's troubles never you
    encumber,
Be blessed with golden sunshine
    and silvery moonbeams.

Sheets are all crumpled,
Blanket on the floor below.
Pillow is rumpled,
Silky locks on velvety skin flow.

The Wink

To the hospital I was rushed for
   it was time to deliver,
This was no heartburn caused by
   fried onions and liver.
I was calm and collected all through
   the ride,
But apprehension Dad-to-Be
   couldn't hide.

Prepared for the occasion and
   surrounded by staff,
The fierce pains were splitting
   me in half.
I remembered my breathing for
   that is important,
Dad-to-Be's trepidations were
   becoming exorbitant.

The final moment came and the
 baby emerged,
Around infant, the medical crew
 converged.
Contractions stopped and I was
 relieved,
It's time to focus on the baby,
 I believed.

This wasn't my first so from
 experience I uttered,
"The baby should be crying," I
 fearfully muttered.
Doctors and nurses turned my way
 for a short blink,
"Little darling is smiling and giving
 us a wink."

The Ultrasound

I'm already eight months into
   my pregnancy,
Weeks ago we've decided on names
   of relevancy.
We diligently looked through many
   a book,
To be prepared with a name we
   undertook.

If the child turns out to be a girl,
She'll be named Alice or Daryl.
If, by chance, the child is male,
He'll be named Dale.

The pregnancy is going well,
  without much turbulence,
I take pride in accomplishing such
  excellence.
This child will be perfect, I have
  no doubt,
And that is surely something to
  rave about.

The time passes slowly but I don't
  really mind,
It gives us the chance to more
  closely bind.
Its gestures are gentle and
  demeanor calm,
I crave so to stroke it with my
  bare palm.

"It'll soon come to pass," I
   repeatedly say,
Caressing the swelling as in bed
   I lay.
In the interim, I attentively listen,
To tiny signals my senses hasten.

As I mentioned before, many months
   have now passed,
But since I last felt my baby some
   hours have lapsed.
Concerned and worried I sharpen
   my senses,
On the alert, my enlarged body
   tenses.

One more hour expires and I still
    feel no movement,
"To the Doctor," I insist and am
    given no argument.
My belly and I are attached to an
    apparatus,
The Ultrasound will explain the
    silent hiatus.

As Doctor glides something on my
    naked belly,
A vision appears on a screen, much
    like a telly.
My eyes are glued to that black
    and white image,
What I behold gives me heart-
    throbbing courage.

The child isn't hurt and no harm
   befell it,
It is calm and serene and of a mild
   spirit.
Though I hadn't sensed it for a
   while today,
It was swimming in its own gentle
   way.

Fearing to blink so as not to miss
   a moment,
My worries have subsided and
   ended my torment.
The child was now waving, or so it
   seemed,
My heart beat with joy as my face
   beamed.

Poor Elsie

Elsie was the center of attention
  until Lizzie came along,
And it seemed so painfully wrong.
The world is no longer her own
  domain,
To reclaim it she tries though in
  vain.

It wasn't at all difficult to see,
While Elsie was an only child, life
  was a glee.
For attention she never needed to
  compete,
But now her parents' time is so
  deplete.

Elsie is hurt and so very bitter,
Because she feels only second to
  her baby sister.
Disheartened and abandoned,
In a situation unamended.

Putting aside jealousy and iration,
Elsie's love for Lizzie adds to her
    irritation.
Lizzie's cute and Elsie can't deny
    the fact,
Her sense of security is no longer
    intact.

Poor dejected Elsie settles for
    whatever she gets,
To deal with what may come her
    mind sets.
When Lizzie's taken for walks in
    an elegant carriage,
Elsie perches on its lower rack,
    the one used for storage.

Selective Hearing

Mom noticed that Bridgette doesn't
   always respond,
And at times her replies don't
   correspond.
What Mom feared most,
Was that Bridgette's hearing was
   lost.

So, as her loving protector,
Mom took Bridgette to the doctor.
Thoughtfully, doctor listened to
   Mom's complaints,
And checked Bridgette's ears with
   no constraints.

Doctor found that the child can
   hear,
And said, "She hears only what
   she wants, I fear."
"Selective hearing is my diagnosis,
It may change with age, is my
   prognosis."

Mommy's Guardian

Years ago I suspected that my
    mother would die,
If I let down my guard and to sleep
    I lie.
More and more tired I would grow,
But to rest I wouldn't go.

At last Mother realized what I was
    doing,
Understood why to sleep I wasn't
    going.
She sat at my side and we had a
    long talk,
Afterwards we got dressed and
    went for a walk.

Mother successfully convinced me,
That after my nap she'd still be.
That she won't leave me for any
    reasons,
That we'd be inseparable for many
    more seasons.

From that day on, to sleep I no
    longer feared,
In different directions my energy
    was now geared.
Carefree and unencumbered,
Thus I peacefully slumbered.

Shopping Cart

All shops in town were crowded for
   a good reason,
It was right in the middle of the
   holiday season.
Mommy walked up and down aisles
   with Timmy at her side,
Passages narrowed by buyers, when
   once they were wide.

Selecting gifts, large and small,
Off the low shelves and the tall.
Bumping and shoving, pushing
   and nudging,
Hurrying and scurrying and rushing
   and dodging.

Mommy had Timmy by the hand,
A dense flow of humanity to
    withstand.
Suddenly, Mommy's arm felt a tug,
"Timmy," she asked. "Do you need
    a hug?"

Hearing no response Mommy
    became leery,
And looked down at her Timmy.
His face was in a flood,
Dripping with bright, red blood.

To her knees, Mommy dropped in
   a hurry,
Her own face paled with concern
   and worry.
Upon close inspection and a deep
   sigh,
Mommy saw the wound in Timmy's
   left eye.

She later realized that Timmy was
   the exact height,
To collide with a shopping cart was
   his inevitable plight.
Wound healed fast, though
   remained scared,
Timmy's good looks were not at all
   marred.

Clever Tricks

Little Stephie hasn't stopped crying
   since the day of her birth,
Persistently wailing to no mirth.
Hearing her weep can break
   anyone's heart,
Inducing painful stabs from the
   start.

Her diaper's been changed and she
   is well fed,
So why is she still yelling in her
   tiny bed?
A doctor examined for disorder,
But found Stephie perfectly in order.

Nonetheless, those attacks are
　　unstopping,
And Stephie's eyes forever need
　　mopping.
Crying and screaming, night and
　　day,
It's so very tiresome to hear her
　　thus bay.

An observed pattern in her shrieks,
Convinced Mom that Stephie is up
　　to some clever tricks.
Howling increases when she's left
　　alone for a moment,
But Mom's reappearance soon
　　relents the torrent.

Whimpering quiets when she's
    mounted,
Atop Mom's arms to and fro carted.
So, Mom gives in to Stephie's every
    yelp,
Oh, but she needs so much help!

Good Morning World

Good morning world! Rise and
    shine!
I feel great! I feel fine!
Marching into the kitchen with
    a light heart,
A robust breakfast I will start.

The rest begin to stir and budge,
In warm beds all awaken with a
    grudge.
Annie and her father step out of
    their night's berth,
It seems so excruciating, much like
    rebirth.

From the washroom into the dinette,
Faces washed and still slightly wet.
I serve Annie's father with eggs and
toast,
She gets cereal because that's what
she likes most.

Now that he's dressed and ready
to go,
Annie's face becomes the ugly visage
I dread so.
This morning won't be different from
any other,
Annie once again won't let go of her
father.

A headache comes on and my
   teeth grit,
Whilst Annie shrieks and throws
   a fit.
Each morning since I can recall,
His departure Annie tries to stall.

She objects to father leaving for
   work,
Kicks and throws herself on the
   floor with a jerk.
I try to calm her again and again,
But all my efforts are in vain.

She knows that he'll return long
    before dark,
Yet on her tantrum she'll daily
    embark.
This morning held so much promise
    for me,
But Annie changed it, as you
    can see.

Gary

Gingerly treading on his way,
Gary practices caution day after
    day.
Looking down with tensed features,
Always on the lookout for little
    creatures.

Gary has made safety of bugs his
    own responsibility,
A burden which gravely confines
    his mobility.
Never stepping where visibility
    is low,
For fear of trampling innocent
    mortals with a careless toe.

Shelley

A trip to the beach was Shelley's
    special treat,
A mini vacation and a day's retreat.
This was her very first visit to the
    seashore,
And so much excitement was in
    store.

On the sun-warmed sand Shelley
    stood,
Joyfully happy and in a great mood.
Posing there with great big eyes,
Asking so many *whats* and *whys*.

"What are the seagulls whispering
   in my ear?"
"And why does it foam like daddy's
   beer?"
"Why does the sand make me walk
   so silly?"
"And when will the wind stop feeling
   so very chilly?"

Time passed and the sea beckoned
   her in,
Gathering courage she took a little
   spin.
An inch at a time advanced forward,
Hesitant but moving onward.

First, the water covered toes, then
    knees and now tummy,
Parents looked on but did not find
    it funny.
They rushed to save Shelley from
    potential drowning,
When her smiling face began
    frowning.

She raised little hands toward
    Daddy to be lifted from the sea,
Safely in his arms, she turned to
    Mommy with a plea.
"Please take me away from here in
    a hurry,"
Shelley's voice was weak
    and blurry.

Mommy and Daddy worriedly
    pondered,
"What has happened?" They
    wondered.
"Are you hurt?" They asked in fear,
Shelley cried, "It stings! And who
    put so much salt in here?"

Jessica-May

Lovely, lively Jessica-May,
Daily skipping home on her merry
   way.

But today was different from the
   rest,
Jessica-May ran home extra fast.

Her face was streaked with tears,
And covered with dirty smears.

I haven't seen the likes in years,
So I enquired about this outpour
   of tears.

"It's Billie," Jessica-May sobbed,
Blew her nose and swollen eyes
   were rubbed.

"Are you hurt?" My heart stopped
   for a moment,
Watching Jessica-May's face full
   of torment.

"I love him and he should be nice,"
"Not spill drinks on me, especially
   full of ice."

Windy and Her Umbrella

Stick around and I shall tell,
About our Windy whom we love so well.
Of her journey home from school one
    day,
Which filled us all with utter dismay.

It was a rainy day in town,
Windy opened her umbrella without
    a frown.
Knowing that Mother had not joked,
When saying, "Please try not to get
    soaked."

Towards home Windy briskly paced,
One step at a time she carefully raced.
Though tempted, puddles Windy
    resisted,
'Cause Mother's words in
    her mind persisted.

She encountered friends on her way,
But didn't stop to play.
Because Mother asked Windy to hurry,
So that she wouldn't have to worry.

Suddenly the weather turned worse,
The wind blew with incredible force.
Windy paraded bravely homeward,
Though more difficult to advance
    onward.

With each step Windy struggled,
From one hand to the other the
    umbrella was juggled.
Holding as tight as could be,
Trudging on, though she could
    hardly see.

The wind became even fiercer,
Windy feared it would pierce her.
Poor little Windy strained along,
Realizing something was very wrong.

That naughty wind, totally unruly,
Picked little Windy up like a bully.
Toes on land were barely kept,
Off the ground she was being swept.

The umbrella by now was completely
    spoiled,
Its spines flipped up, its cloth ripped
    and soiled.
It no longer protected our Windy from
    dripping,
But continued
    flop flipping.

Mischief

Sporty Marty

Sporty Marty, out playing ball,
Bouncing and skipping off ground
   and wall,
As the game becomes boring,
Into the house Marty comes roaring.

"My arm's broken and hurts!" He
   weeps,
Smudges off tearful face sweeps,
Mommy and Daddy anxiously race,
Marty's "broken" arm to face.

No swelling nor cut, no bruise nor
   abrasion,
They inspect his arm with concerned
   invasion,
Though Marty claims severe pain,
Mommy and Daddy are
   looking in vain.

To ER they rush the wailing child,
And there he becomes increasingly
    wild,
Heartbreaking shrieks to Marty's
    side steer,
One, two and three doctors who
    over the "broken" arm peer.

Each probe invites new whimpers
    and groans,
Runny-nosed, Marty dramatically
    moans,
Doctors examine and confirm their
    doubt,
While Marty continues to squirm
    about.

Prudently, doctors suggest an
   X-ray be taken,
Of the arm which they suspect not
   "broken,"
The image proves what doctors
   already see,
Marty's "broken" arm is well as
   can be.

To appease Marty and his unharmed
   appendage,
Doctors wrap it with a big white
   bandage,
The unbroken arm is taken home in
   a dressing,
While Marty's grunts are continually
   pressing.

Soon the three arrive home with
  relief,
End of my story is beyond belief,
Upon entering front door of the
  house,
Marty grabs the ball quietly as a
  mouse.

Swiftly he unwinds the big white
  wrapping,
Rendering his parents helplessly
  gapping,
Once again, Sporty Marty is out
  playing ball,
Bouncing and skipping off ground
  and wall.

Mabel McGuire

Visiting with neighbors is something
  I do very seldom,
But this day I needed to alleviate some
  boredom.
Mabel has been ill so doctor suggested
  we stay confined,
Now that she's better we both needed
  to unwind.

Off to visit Tina, up the stairs we
  climbed,
And on her doorbell chimed.
Tina bid us to enter,
Pleased to see me and my youngster.

"Biscuits?" Tina graciously proposed,
Assuring us we hadn't imposed.
Into the kitchen, Tina escorted
  Mabel and me,
Also offering a cup of tea.

I sat bouncing Mabel on my lap,
But she wouldn't be restrained in such
a trap.
She wiggled and squirmed until I let
her sprawl,
On Tina's kitchen floor I let her crawl.

Tina and I sat around the table,
At our feet was gurgling little Mabel.
We chatted while the clock ticked
minutes away,
I was pleased to be having such a good
day.

At some point in time, I recall with a
chill,
Tina and I realized it was much too still.
Looking down at the floor beneath our
feet,
There was no one there for our eyes
to greet.

We jumped off our seats for my child
   to look,
Searching through the condo in every
   crevice and nook.
Mabel wasn't to be found but the front
   door was ajar,
We dashed for it hoping she hadn't
   gone far.

Passing neighboring doors we knocked
   to inquire,
"Has anyone seen little Mabel
   McGuire?"
Down three flights of stairs we ran
   faster than we should,
To find Mabel we prayed that we would.

No sooner had we reached street level,
We heard cooing and giggling in revel.
The sounds were coming from the trash
    room,
Amongst rubbish my child has come
    to no doom.

How she got there is anyone's guess,
The fact that I found her unharmed
    is all I'll stress.
She probably crawled and glided on
    her tummy,
Relieved, I lifted her off the floor putrid
    and gummy.

Puppy's Bowl

Laboring in the kitchen a great deal,
Mommy prepared a wonderful meal.

It contained the choicest ingredients,
   vitamins and minerals,
A feast fit for kings and high ranked
   admirals.

But Nancy refused her lips to part,
When Mommy offered the spoon from
   the start.

Repeatedly, Mommy attempted to feed
   Nancy,
But something else always caught the
   child's fancy.

In the corner of the room, Nancy
    observed,
Her puppy, by Daddy, was being served.

From her highchair she jumped,
Determined, to her puppy Nancy
    stumped.

Looking down at her puppy's food,
To eat she was suddenly in the mood.

Her puppy's grub seemed so sweet,
Out of his bowl Nancy began to eat.

Chocolate Chip Cookies

Nellie was a habitual cause for
    aggravation,
Turning each meal into one long
    agitation.
She was never hungry for healthy food,
Good nutrition hadn't yet understood.

I, her mother, tried my very best,
Preparing favorites for Nellie, I was put
    to the test.
But the child never approve of my
    cooking at all,
And I feared she'd stop growing and
    remain small.

Coaxing and cajoling didn't do the trick,
So I tried that old *carrot and the stick.*
It helped none at all and I was at my
  wit's end,
Seemingly, to my child I knew not how
  to tend.

Feeling the failure, I helplessly raised
  my hands,
Praying that someday Nellie
  understands.
It wasn't that she boasted no appetite,
But put up a stance of power and
  sheer spite.

The moment I turned from the food
   before Nellie,
She groaned and complained of an
   ache in her belly.
Her stomach growled for sustenance
   it was needing,
In desperation, I once again suggested
   a feeding.

Nellie would have nothing to do with
   what I was serving,
And self-control I was barely preserving.
The moment I allowed Nellie to leave the
   dining room table,
She jumped on a stool so to reach she'd
   be able.

What Nellie was stretching so hard
   to attain,
Were chocolate chip cookies which
   she wished to obtain.
It was plain to see that Nellie was
   famished,
But the food I served was rudely
   banished.

A Day at the Beach

A day at the beach is always so much
fun,
To swim in the water and on the sand
run.

There're thousands of seashells to be
gathered,
Multitudes of people to be bothered.

The beach and its wonders never cease,
Rushing waves and sandy shores tease.

Sand castles need to be built,
Swishing bare toes without guilt.

Sailboats on the horizon must never
be overlooked,
Blue skies above, and seagulls to be
spooked.

One can always rest on striped lounge
    chairs,
Pretend one is grown and put on all
    kinds of airs.

Attentive ears can enjoy a festival of
    noises,
And watch mankind sunbathing in all
    kinds of poses.

And how can the cooler be disregarded?
Especially when Mommy leaves it
    unguarded.

Well, all that for Jeffrey was not
    enough,
Boredom made staying out of trouble
    tough.

Handfuls of sand into his mouth Jeffrey
    shoved,
Getting the attention he wanted and
    loved.

He paid for his silliness when a tummy
    ache started,
For the next two days Jeffrey cramped
    and smarted.

Tammy and Her Staff

Tammy is a whimsical child,
Her inclinations never mild.
And if truth must be told,
She's mostly frightfully bold.

Capricious, flighty, daring and
 brash,
Tammy will trample, bump and
 smash.
Mom and Dad caution to no end,
Admonitions endlessly send.

"Tammy, please watch where you're
 going!"
"Don't jump and slow down your
 running!"
Realizing their warnings are useless,
Mom and Dad are rendered totally
 powerless.

Let me tell you about a particular
   day,
When Mom and Dad watched
   Tammy at play.
She chased an imaginary enemy
   with a long staff,
Intending to stab it in half.

Straight toward a wall Tammy
   dashed,
Into an unyielding barrier she
   and staff crashed.
The staff broke upon impact with
   a din,
But not before it punctured
   Tammy's tender skin.

Staff fell to the ground, splintered,
Brightly crimson, Tammy glittered.
Persistent wailing never hushed,
While to the hospital Tammy was
    rushed.

Just as Mom nearly swooned,
The doctor finished dressing
    Tammy's wound.
They were sent home with assurance
    that all was well,
When next they'd have to return to
    the ER no one could foretell.

The Birthday Party

Rachel's fifteenth birthday was coming
  up,
For the sake of the party other projects
  had to stop.
This was going to be a magnificently
  fun activity,
All of her friends were to attend this
  festivity.

The refrigerator was filled with salads,
  dips and lots to drink,
The freezer above it was loaded with
  ice cream to its brink.
They decorated the house with bright
  balloons in preparation of the day,
Hung multicolored crepe paper and
  moved furniture out
  of the way.

That wonderful day finally came with
  relief,
All was prepared with efficiency beyond
  belief.
The procession of gift-bearing young
  guests lasted for a while,
Rachel received each caller with a big
  happy smile.

The house was now filled to a
  maximum,
Noises merged to an ear splitting hum.
Youth meandered, chatted and snacked
  all about,
As the buzzing increased, so did Mom
  and Dad's doubt.

Rachel warned her parents to stay out
  of sight,
Forbidding them to appear this night.
Through their bedroom walls they heard
  the clatter,
But weren't able to tell what was the
  matter.

At last, in the wee hours of the night,
The house fell asleep just before
  morning's light.
All was silent and suspiciously hushed,
A nasty odor through the house gushed.

Just outside their bedroom door,
Mom and Dad could hardly see the
    floor.
Feet slipped and glided through
    unidentified slush,
Each step encountered nothing but
    gooey mush.

Walls in every room were colorfully
    enriched,
With smeared berries, and fudge and
    slivers of peach.
The few pieces of furniture that were left
    in their place,
Were now stuffed with produce and took
    on an alien face.

Lampshades were finger painted with
chocolate and jam,
A half-eaten bagel in the fish tank
swam.
Bookshelves were crowded with
bananas and chips,
Piano keys were garnished with parsley
snips.

Gingerly and with caution Mom toured
her ravaged home,
Outraged eyes over destroyed residence
roam.
To open the refrigerator Mom braved,
Its gutted cavity brazenly at her raved.

No More Trikes

In timeout corners Jackie and Jillie
    were left seated,
After riding trikes in the house, which
    wasn't permitted.
Regardless, they decided to have their
    own will,
Intending to ride through the house till
    they've had their fill.

Mom was nearly knocked down while
    preparing a meal,
The long knife in her hand was made of
    sinister steel.
Jackie and Jillie froze centered to the
    kitchen floor,
Because Mom blocked their flight
    through the open door.

Mom slashed the six tires with her
   sharp blade,
Rendering trikes impotent and children
   cowering in their shade.
Having done what she did and perhaps
   somewhat satisfied,
Mom knew that with those trikes she'd
   never again be defied.

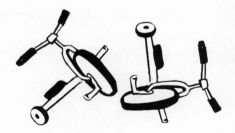

Daddy's New Radio

Curiosity is an admirable quality, you
    must agree,
Driving our Mark to thoroughly examine
    and see.

Mark seeks out all that he can,
Scrutinizing with no apparent plan.

Into boxes and drawers Mark gets,
Windows and doors undoes and resets.

His mind will never rest,
Reaching for answers with energetic
    zest.

Ah! Mark just noticed Daddy's new
    radio,
Now standing on a table in the patio.

Whether he tried or not we'll never
    know,
Temptation wouldn't let our Mark go.

Unscrewing and twisting and snapping
    apart,
Mark was checking the radio's heart.

Spying on little people talking within,
Removing radio's parts with much noise
    and din.

Daddy came running to see what the
    commotion was about,
Horrified witnessing his radio's guts
    being ripped out.

There on a table lay the decapitated
    new radio,
Resigned, Daddy shuffled
    away from the patio.

Muppy and Her Puppy

Mommy needed shopping one lovely
   day,
Having much to do, she wished no
   delay.

Into the stroller she placed toddler
   Muppy,
And on Muppy's lap she sat the puppy.

They both had a tendency to jump,
   Mommy well knew,
So into the stroller she tied the two.

Muppy was secured with a harness
   though she put up a fight,
Puppy with a leash was bonded to
   abort a potential flight.

Mommy attempted crossing a busy
   boulevard with all her might,
But livestock from the stroller spilled
   left and right.

Muppy, though harnessed, jumped
   to one side,
While leashed puppy in the other
   direction swung wide.

On her harness Muppy remained
   dangling,
On the leash the puppy was hanging.

In the middle of a traffic-laden
   boulevard,
To collect child and puppy
   Mommy tried hard.

The cars were rushing every which way,
Horns were honking and all was in
    disarray.

Mommy decided that the safest thing
    to do,
Was clear that boulevard with no
    further ado.

Accelerating her pace to reach the
    safety of a sidewalk,
To save her load Mommy could no
    longer balk.

With Muppy still dangling and the
    puppy hanging daftly,
Mommy and her burden finally reached
    safety.

A Bike Race

Michelle is an energetic seven-year-
   old,
Outrageously mischievous and bold.
She can't resist the temptation to
   partake,
In challenges, no matter what is
   at stake.

Of consequence Michelle never
   thinks,
From dangerous enterprises never
   shrinks.
I try to stop her but my efforts are
   in vain,
She just won't listen and that is
   plain.

One afternoon I stood at the window
    sill,
Watching Michelle ride her bike
    down a hill.
She was racing a much older boy,
So out the window I shouted,
    "Ahoy!"

I implored Michelle to stop her
    foolish endeavor,
But, of course, she thought she
    was more clever.
Michelle ignored my cries of
    admonition,
She'd have nothing to do with my
    premonition.

She sped down the hill determined
　　to win the contest,
Knowing it useless, I gave up
　　further protest.
With a prayer in my heart and a
　　watchful eye,
I remained at the window to
　　helplessly spy.

Suddenly, a gruesome nightmare
　　flashed before me,
Wobbling downhill a riderless bike
　　was all I could see.
Michelle wasn't on it because into
　　a parked car she suddenly bolted,
And its antenna a crash to the
　　ground halted.

Chin jammed hard into the
    antenna's protruding metal,
Dangling and thrashing, her body
    found no saddle.
As the bike continued its downward
    motion,
Michelle remained suspended in
    convulsion.

With wind in my wings and frost
    in my heart,
Daftly I ran to tear Michelle and
    antenna apart.
Affront to the chin was deep,
But not terribly serious and she
    didn't even weep.

Home from the Zoo

My story is about Mary Lou,
Who was taken one day to the zoo.
When the trip was announced,
Joyously Mary Lou bounced.

A picnic basket was packed,
Food and drinks were stacked.
Mary Lou couldn't sleep the night
    before the outing,
It all sounded so very exciting.

Mary Lou admired animals in their
    cages,
She, a child amongst others of all ages.
Mary Lou looked with amazement
    and awe,
At birds, tigers and little
    monkeys on a see-saw.

Swinging and hopping, leaping and
    jumping,
Springing and skipping, pouncing and
    romping.
Everyone looked on with pleasure,
Having fun spying on nature's treasure.

The following day rather grim,
After yesterday's outing all seemed
    too dim.
So Mary Lou attempted to mimic the
    zoo,
Causing Mommy to panic and so
    would you.

Suspended low from the ceiling,
To receive Mary Lou the crystal
    chandelier was willing.
It hung above the living room table,
In splendor it dangled on a gold-plated
    cable.

Unable to resist the alluring fixture,
Mary Lou embarked on her venture.
Up on the glass-top a stool was placed,
Mary Lou climbed and her hands
    upward raised.

At the chandelier Mary Lou grabbed,
Fingers held tight while feet at the air
    stabbed.
In imitation of little monkeys
    at the zoo,
Swinging and swaying
    proceeded Mary Lou.

Mischief *CS* 139

Scissors in Hand

My pretty little Harriet,
Disposition calm and quiet.
Decided your appearance needed
    revision,
Over your hair you took supervision.

Scissors in hand,
Before the mirror you took a stand.
Off with that unwanted hair, chop,
    chop,
Snip, snap, pop, pop.

The forehead once bare,
Is now covered with scraggly hair.
The floor paved with rejected coils,
At your feet lie the discarded spoils.

My pretty little Harriet,
Disposition calm and quiet.
Unclad forehead or attired with tresses,
I'll always give you loving caresses.

No need to alter your looks for me,
I love you as you are, and as you
    will be.
In my eyes you shall always and forever
    appear,
Pretty little Harriet, and I hope that
    is clear.

Lesley's Revenge

It was anger that drove Daddy to
    slap Lesley's hand,
He just couldn't continue her
    behavior to stand.
She just wouldn't stop being catty,
All the while driving Daddy more
    and more batty.

Daddy doesn't hit Lesley very often,
For he knows how his temper to
    soften.
But Lesley habitually continues
    disturbing,
She just didn't know when to
    stop perturbing.

Well, on this particular occasion
    Daddy couldn't help himself,
Lesley, time and time again,
    removed books off his shelf.
She took each book between sticky
    fingers and at the pages slashed,
Leaving them hopelessly trashed.

The books were valuable in Daddy's
    eye,
And to stop Lesley he'd once again
    try.
Lesley didn't listen to his pleas for
    cooperation,
So he slapped her hand out of sheer
    exasperation.

Unaccustomed to Daddy's act of
    sudden violence,
Lesley wouldn't settle for
    compliance.
She decided to get revenge on Daddy
    this day,
Why such drastic measures I
    couldn't say.

Sharp fingernails Lesley dug deeply,
Scratching the back of her own
    hand steeply.
Wounding and drawing blood,
Her hand sopped in a bright red
    flood.

Lesley rushed to show Mommy her
    injury,
"Daddy did it," such was her brazen
    perjury.
Lesley hoped Daddy'd be scolded
    and thus get satisfaction,
But Mommy didn't believe Daddy's
    infraction.

Unwilling to dwell on such
    falsehood,
Mommy quietly cleansed Lesley's
    injury real good.
Daddy's expression was painfully
    sad,
While lovingly patting Lesley on
    the head.

Not a word was ever said about
    Lesley's attempt at retaliation,
Nor reference made to her mutilated
    hand and its initiation.
Soon the hand healed of its affront,
    leaving no particular scar,
Father and daughter alliance
    recovered and is now stronger
    by far.

Trisha Wins Again

Exhausting all options and for lack
   of anything else to do,
I desperately sought medical advice
   and counseling too.
I took my three-year-old Trisha for
   a psychiatric evaluation,
Needing expert advice in such a
   disagreeable situation.

The good doctor told me that the
   best thing would be,
To ignore the little culprit and
   pretend misconduct not to see.
"Her tantrums," the doctor claimed,
   "are nurtured and sustained,"
"Each time they are dignified with
   a response, genuine or feigned."

"It makes little difference whether
reactions are positive or otherwise,"
"They invite additional tantrums,
    at times larger by twice."
I paid the doctor and it was quite
    costly,
So I took his advice because I had
    little to lose, mostly.

The very next time Trisha hurled
    into her typical tantrum,
Noisy clatter was familiar and
    annoyingly humdrum.
Turning my back, I continued about
    my own business,
She commenced screaming but
    didn't have me as an eye witness.

As doctor prescribed, I turned deaf
ears to Trisha's clamor,
She, in turn, accelerated with a roar
and a tremor.
I grated my teeth, clenched my fists
and continued to neglect,
Trisha's misbehavior I proceeded to
deflect.

Finally and after what seemed like
hours on end,
Trisha slowed her torrent as if
drained of vigor to spend.
Feeling the loss of power and
strength,
To spare herself defeat
she went at length.

Kicking, thrashing and banging her
    head on the floor,
None of it got the attention she was
    striving for.
Out of exhaustion and sheer
    frustration,
Trisha sank sharp teeth into my
    shin with indignation.

Triumph and success! She once
    again won the battle,
Trisha managed my stamina to
    rattle.
Forgetting all that doctor had
    admonished,
A stormy downpour I furiously
    furnished.

Wallops on the Hind

Stevie is unruly and a menacing
   handful,
Mischievous, energetic and willful.
Frequent punishments earns,
But never really learns.

Wallops on the hind he got many,
None set him straight nor improved
   behavior any.
Spankings relieve Mom and Dad,
Somewhat easing rage at their
   turbulent lad.

TV is Stevie's favorite pastime at
   home,
Keeping him seated like a good
   little gnome.
It has lots to offer and much
   To   be learned,
At which times even
   snacks are spurned.

Stevie watches programs for hours
  on end,
To keep out of trouble and boredom
  to fend.
He's by now an expert mimic of
  stars,
From exotic kings to Russian Tsars.

Yesterday the TV busted and there
  was little else to occupy Stevie's
  time,
So he uprooted Mom's potted plants
  and atop furniture proceeded to
  climb.
Stevie ignored Mom when she said,
  "Please stop this, dear."
So she reached out and smacked his
  little rear.

Unwilling to succumb to childish
    crying,
Stevie grabbed at his chest and
    began deeply sighing.
He then proceeded groaning and
    dramatically moaning,
Arousing Mom's anxiety and
    warning.

Seeing the effect on Mom he was
    making,
Stevie continued his heart attack
    faking.
Being the talented little actor that
    he was,
He convinced Mom that of great
    damage she was the cause.

Head Dive

"Enough is enough," I finally had
    to say,
But Joey continued on and on all
    day.

Constantly juggling, spinning and
    whirling,
Endlessly jumping, skipping and
    twirling.

On my king-size bed Joey bravely
    stood,
Beneath his feet a mattress while
    below, bare hardwood.

Side to side, back and forth,
Joey's arms swung east to west
    and south to north.

Knees slightly bent,
Joey's body forward went.

Oh no! It's a head dive! But you
    must recall,
Down below was nothing but the
    unforgiving floor.

I gathered the child into my arm,
Relieved and thankful that he
    came to no harm.

Olivia Flirts

Little Olivia is the smallest in our
    neighborhood,
But seems to be the biggest cause
    for many a feud.
She and other tots in the local
    playground,
Play hide-and-seek, skip rope and
    run around.

Though seemingly well adjusted
    there is something amiss,
Olivia's behavior is unacceptably
    remiss.
The cause and reason are
    completely mysterious to me,
I'm just an amateur, you see.

Olivia flirts with children twice her
    age,
Hits them from behind and arouses
    their rage.
Once a blow is delivered to an
    unsuspecting hind,
Olivia's hands are concealed at her
    own behind.

The startled victim looks for
    someone to blame,
Olivia stands there innocently tame.
One of these days, as a matter of
    fact,
She'll be caught in her unwarranted
    act.

I fear the outcome of that inevitable
day,
When Olivia is forced to heavily pay.
She would have deserved it, what
ever it be,
But her pain will also be painful
to me.

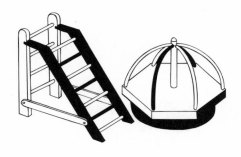

Nickie Flipped

When my Nickie was born the house
    filled with glee,
We were so proud of ourselves, you
    see.
Our lives now revolved around this
    sweet little tyke,
Everything she did we couldn't help
    but like.

Days and weeks passed much too
    rapidly,
Nickie developed and grew
    intrepidly.
Managed to sit up all by herself,
Crawling came easy to our little elf.

A few more weeks pass and Nickie
  stands,
One uncertain foot ahead of the
  other demands.
At times she'll succeed at others
  she'll fail,
More often than not, Nickie ends
  on her tail.

Nickie is twelve months of age,
And is now at the walking stage.
Cooing and gurgling advance to
  gibberish,
Our tiny tyke has matured but
  isn't yet girlish.

In her crib Nickie still sleeps,
Where she's protected from falling
  out in heaps.
We believed her too young for a
  juvenile's bed,
Failing to think clearly or planning
  ahead.

Though Nickie's been appearing
  from the crib on her own,
We gave it no thought nor realized
  she's outgrown.
Finally we admitted that she must
  urgently be promoted,
When her exodus from the crib was
  alarmingly noted.

Over the crib's guarding rails Nickie
   flipped,
Onto the floor she pounced and
   skipped.
Thus was firmly decided, to avoid
   situations that could be fatal,
Nickie will no longer sleep in an
   infant's cradle.

Randy Swallowed a Coin

Randy inserted a silver coin into his
    mouth,
As do many children in the North,
    Midwest and down South.

Mom tried to persuade him with the
    change to part,
But Randy's mouth just wouldn't
    unload nor depart.

From side to side, around and around,
Busy tongue, a plaything found.

At times the right cheek swelled with
    fullness, at others it was the left,
Mom's force reaped no fruits though
    her efforts were deft.

Struggle they did, Randy and Mom,
That proved unwise and even outright
    dumb.

It was Randy's sudden look of surprise,
Mom read the news in his wide open
    eyes.

The coin descended down Randy's
    throat,
Swallowed and slipped through his
    bodily moat.

Worried and angry, Mom took Randy
    to the clinic,
All the while her frustration increasing
    and turning to panic.

An X-ray confirmed the presence of
    money,
It did indeed go down Randy's alley.

Doc directed an inspection of each
    movement of bowel,
Poor Mom was assigned through
    excrement to prowl.

Days later a familiar object was found,
It was flat, shiny, and round.
This was the swallowed coin which
    emerged,
Randy's body had the foreign
    object purged.

Sam-the-Ham

My child, I must admit, is such
   a little ham,
Loves attention, that's my little
   Sam.
The more people look at him the
   better,
Thrives on admiration from any
   spectator.

An audience for Sam is bread and
   butter,
He'll dance, sing and even stutter.
There is really very little our
   Sam-the-Ham won't do,
To be admired by you and you
   and you.

On the way home from town,
   a bus we took,
Sam glanced about and then went
   back for still another look.
Centered in the bus, Sam took
   a stance.
To assess his potential fans.

The bus was packed with people
   of all sorts,
Sam appraised them all as good
   sports.
But now he must plan and
   strategize,
"What will earn me most of the
   eyes?"

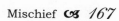

The bus was about to move on its
  way,
I led Sam to an empty seat without
  further delay.
There, Sam didn't stay very long,
A busload of people prodded him
  along.

Sam was on a quest and an urgent
  mission,
And, of course, failed to wait for
  my permission.
He stood erect on the seat,
And proceeded with a cheerful
  tweet.

Small fists grabbed at the overhead
   rack,
Feet swung back and forth then
   forth and back.
In an off-key peal his childish voice
   broke about,
Sam's audience was well sought out.

Every eye on that bus focused on
   my Sam,
One and all thought him cute
   though a bit of a ham.
Indifferent, they all loved to observe,
But I feared a fall, so braced myself
   to serve.

Nature Calls

Teenage Daughters

We have a couple of teenage daughters
    in the house,
Proudly parenting two lovely girls, I and
    my spouse.
To the phone and the bathroom we just
    cannot get,
Because our teens monopolize the set.

Those modern facilities are unfairly
    shared,
For us they are begrudgingly spared.
We literally have to plead for
    permission,
To use what we pay for we must submit
    a petition.

On the phone they converse every
    waking moment,
Mostly cheerful but at times a lengthy
    torrent.
The bathroom serves well for many
    various tasks,
To bathe, read or apply their facial
    masks.

Don't think for a moment that they lack
    coordination,
They're quite able to combine the two
    wonders of civilization.
The phone can reach all corners of the
    bathroom,
Behind closed doors they disappear
    and won't emerge till we boom.

And just when we think they are done
    for now,
They go back for more, disregarding
    our uplifted brow.
We try to race them but of course they
    always beat us,
And fail to understand our indignation
    and fuss.

Getting back on the phone for one more
    word of importance,
Returning to the bathroom for one
    additional admittance.
Our needs are not significant thus easy
    to ignore,
Our frequent complaints are by now a
    total bore.

We got a two-bathroom house thinking
    things would improve,
A second telephone line we ordered
    immediately with the move.
The phones and the bathrooms are
    still out of reach,
We acquired a private bathroom and
    phone for each!

They are happier now, for we've
    eliminated the need to share,
They each have their own and we still
    don't get the spare.
If truth be told, it has gotten worse for
    my spouse and me,
We still don't get what we pay for and
    we now pay double, you see.

Donna's Braid

Donna's braid is perpetually wet,
To solve this dilemma Mom's mind
  was set.

She watched and endlessly observed,
To unravel the mystery she deserved.

Spying Donna's every movement,
Mom finally uncovered the riddle with
  some amusement.

As Donna sat on the toilet seat,
Bottom deep in its cavity, in the air
  dangling feet.

Donna's long braid was suspended
  far down her back,
Its tip floated in the
  water with slack.

Ever-Spreading Puddle

This is a plea to adults who with
   children interact,
Be flexible and with more compassion
   please act.
I'm turning to you as one grown-up to
   another,
Whether you're a teacher, an uncle
   or a mother.

As children, you were controlled by big
   people around you,
Without their permission there was
   little you could do.
Now that I've taken you down memory
   lane,
Allow me to share an incident which
   caused me much
   undue pain.

It was in third grade, I remember
     vividly,
Recalling the episode still angers me
     lividly.
I cannot forgive it though I try to,
That is the reason I'm appealing to you.

At roll call for P.E. we stood,
Uniformed and in formation as we
     should.
Teacher called names one by one
     alphabetically,
We responded "here" and all
     commenced systematically.

My friend raised a meek hand in the air,
Requesting to be excused she had
     courage to dare.
Teacher complied with no justification,
My friend dashed out with glee and
     elation.

Time passed and Teacher continued
    name calling,
Each of us responded without further
    stalling.
Then another girl's hand went up,
Teacher nodded and out she rushed
    with a skip and a hop.

As this roll call went on and on,
I now too needed to be gone.
Up went my hand for permission to
    be excused,
Teacher shot me a glance surprisingly
    confused.

I guess she thought these exits were
    a plot of some sort,
And ceased being the good sport.
She told me to wait for the dismissal
    bell,
Disappointed, my spirits fell.

Class wouldn't be finished for a long
    time passing,
Meanwhile my urge was becoming more
    pressing.
My bladder was calling louder and more
    strongly insistent,
Power to fight off the need was
    becoming nonexistent.

I held on by pressing my knees tight
   as could be,
Fists and eyes clenched till I hurt and
   could hardly see.
I shifted and hobbled from left foot to
   right,
But solace and relief were nowhere in
   sight.

Desperately I attempted again to ask,
In my discomfort, this was no easy task.
Teacher glanced coldly in my direction,
But ignored my bold infraction.

Alas, I could no longer deny my plight,
Knowing I had lost the fight.
My life was now in a sorry muddle,
Because I was standing in an ever-
   spreading puddle.

Pete Showered Me!

The house is laden with relatives,
They all came to visit the family.
Wearing party festives,
Sitting back relaxing lazily.

Grandma, grandpa, aunties and
    cousins,
On coaches and chairs recline.
Discussing sport games, *outs* and *ins,*
With ease and pleasure all align.

Mommy serves cookies, cake and fruits,
Daddy pours wine all the while.
Into conversation Grandpa everyone
    recruits,
Elation and laughter continually
    compile.

Suddenly, they sense a peculiar scent,
Familiar yet very disturbing.
They can no longer remain complacent,
As the revolting aroma grows more
    perturbing.

Into the room comes little Billie
    dripping,
The smell is so bad they gasp with
    annoyance.
On the floor his feet sloshing and
    slipping,
Somehow he manages to retain balance.

"Pete showered me with his wee-wee,"
Billie announces rather proudly.
From that pungent odor guests wish
   to flee,
But Mommy's and Daddy's silence
   cautions them loudly.

Disgraced, Mommy glances at her
   guests' faces,
Daddy becomes harsh and forbidding.
In fear, out of the house Pete races,
Innocent Billie thinks they are all
   kidding.

Rancid Stream

Cuddly, snuggly, Gracie, baby,
Chubby, chunky, pudgy, tubby.
Gracie needed diapers changing,
And her apparel rearranging.

Mommy confronted the chore with
    tender loving,
Gracie's clothes started removing.
As soon as Gracie's privates were free,
She cooed and gurgled and chattered
    with glee.

Up in the air, dimply feet Gracie kicked,
With dumpy fingers tiny toes tricked.
Gracie's tummy Mommy tickled,
Rounded bottom gently prickled.

Oh, but what happened? What has
   gone wrong?
That facial contortion does not belong.
Bright eyes tightly fastened,
Miniature smile to a frown hastened.

What Mommy discovered you may not
   trust,
All she could do is laugh till she bust.
In her freedom, Gracie let out a rancid
   stream,
With sour liquid, her face was agleam.

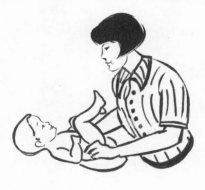

Heidi and Paige

At three years of age,
Accidents still befall Paige.

So, fantasies Paige invents,
To save face are her intents.

"Heidi made in my panties again,"
The fable is quite innocently plain.

Of course Heidi didn't stain Paige's
    panties,
And I trust the accusations will stop
    much before their twenties.

Inquisitive Vicki

To dry the dishes mother left Vicki
    in the playpen one afternoon,
Told her to behave and promised
    to come get her soon.

Vicki and playpen were in the family-
    room,
It was safe and the child could come
    to no doom.

From the open-door kitchen mother
    was able to watch over the child,
As she was completing her chore and
    continually smiled.

The clock ticked away some time,
Out of the playpen Vicki attempted
    to climb.

Unsuccessful and discouraged,
Through all that she could Vicki
    rummaged.

Exhausting all sources of investigation,
To her gorged diaper she turned
    undivided attention.

Reaching both hands deep inside,
A load was heaved far and wide.

Smearing herself, the playpen and all,
Never missing the floor below nor the
    nearby wall.

Little Helper

Adults always tell Tillie to do her
    chores,
Most of the time they're dreadful bores.

One day Grandma asked her to sweep
    the floor,
An aunt told her to wipe a stain off
    a door.

Pick up the toys and take out the trash,
There're always plenty of dishes to
    splash.

Don't forget to scrape from under the
    nails,
Wipe your shoes if you stepped on
    snails.

And you must never ever forget,
To wash behind your ears or the dirt
   will set.

Early one morning before dawn,
Tillie stretched and released a yawn.

Mamma's little helper she decided
   to be,
Creatively decisive was she.

Her baby sister in the crib,
Needed a feeding and a bib.

But a diaper must first be arranged,
For the baby needs a change.

Tillie climbed into where baby slept,
Her promise to help must be kept.

Two tiny ankles in one hand she
    attempted to grasp,
Just as she's seen Mamma many
    times clasp.

One hand is too small to hold onto the
    two,
Lifting one ankle with both hands will
    have to do.

Mamma rushed to release an upside-
    down baby from Tillie's grip,
Fearing that onto the floor baby would
    tip.

Our Roy

A very bright child is this boy,
Clever and smart is our Roy.

As far back as Roy can bring to mind,
He's always been told never to leave
    messes behind.

It seems the whole adult world had
    a single whim,
To train our Roy to be neat and trim.

One weekend we decided on a picnic
    to embark,
A basket and a cooler full of food took
    to the park.

Friends, young and old, met us in
  the park,
Daddy promised we'd stay till after
  dark.

We all ate and played and had a grand
  time,
Danced and sang a song or two in
  rhyme.

Shortly before the picnic was spent,
In search of a bathroom Roy went.

Unsuccessful and unable to wait for
  another moment,
Roy could put up with no more torment.

Out of Mommy's basket Roy nabbed,
Paper napkins and a plastic bag he
    grabbed.

To find more privacy Roy must,
To do what he needed before he bust.

Done and finished with nature's call,
Roy gathered his product in a tidy ball.

Back into Mommy's basket Roy's mess
    went,
Its pungent odor to all a message sent.

So, our Roy did what he needed,
And to our teachings obediently heeded.

Infant Michael

In a crib lies a bundle of joy,
A seemingly helpless tiny boy.
For food and shelter on parents relies,
But outward appearance the world
    belies.

Michael is in complete control,
He isn't really powerless at all.
He decides when to sleep,
When to smile and when to weep.

Mommy is needed to prepare a feeding
    bottle,
But for her, that can become a losing
    battle.
He can't change his own soiled diaper,
    that is quite true,
But he's capable of making Mommy
    blue.

I believe that he's come to the
    conclusion,
Not to readily part with his diaper
    of profusion.
He's made up his tiny mind,
To his Mommy to be unkind.

When Michael's diaper needed to
    be changed,
Thus Mommy became engaged.
Soon she realized the futility of her
    endeavor,
While holding onto her child with fervor.

Michael twisted and turned and flipped
    from back to tummy,
Little fists groped, dimply legs kicked
    at Mommy.
He swung and pounced from hip to hip,
All the while a smile on each tiny lip.

Mommy dreaded his bouncing like
a rounded, rubber ball,
Fearing his wild movements will cause
a fall.
To the floor she moved him, away from
potential falling,
Michael continued thrashing and
rolling.

Ultimately, Mommy called Daddy to
her side,
Needing assistance, defeat she could
no longer hide.
It took two adults to overpower one tiny
body,
The infant was the victor and that is
the parody.

Monkey-See-Monkey-Do

Children are little monkey-see-monkey-
    doers,
As we know so well, they're copycatters.

With that in mind, you'll understand
    why Lisa did what she did,
When I saw and heard what I did from
    my kid.

Yesterday Lisa followed her brother to
    the restroom twice or more,
And awaited his exit from behind the
    closed door.

Today, from the bathroom we heard
a strange sound,
Upon investigation, at the toilet bowl
Lisa was found.

Fists clenched and face flushed,
stiffened body hailed,
Tensing in front of the cold utensil,
Lisa wailed.

To mimic her brother she attempted,
Oblivious to the fact that little girls
are exempted.

Besides, it wasn't to pee that she was
straining,
But a movement of bowel she wished
to be attaining.

Toilet Training

Mommies and Daddies throughout
the universe,
Into toilet training toddlers much
energy immerse.

More time and effort is invested into
diaper weaning,
Than into teaching children writing
and reading.

Little Harry finally agreed to try his pan,
The diaper he too wished to ban.

After a while Harry rose with pants still
around his feet,
Potty obviously empty, hobbled away
surprisingly discreet.

Mommy and Daddy looked down to
   where he was previously seated,
Into a fresh diaper Harry was fitted.

The child realized his parents' chagrin
   at their little offender,
Made up his mind, "Next time I'll try
   even harder."

The following day he was again seated
   on the pot,
Staying until the seat got unbearably
   hot.

Unable to remain so still,
He stood up but that pot didn't fill.

Suddenly, Harry had the urge to
   unburden his load,
Down he squatted as droppings fell
   to the floorboard.

Uncomfortable and filled with
    embarrassment,
Poor Harry was in an awkward
    predicament.

Moving away to drop another pile,
Helplessly remorseful all the while.

Forsaking that site he moved a foot
    or two,
Additional mounds were dropped by
    you know who.

Heavy hearted, Daddy observed while
    Mommy broke out in weeps,
In the center of the room they counted
    a half a dozen heaps.

Upside-Down Child

Being as old as I am you'd think
    I would have learned by now,
You can't predict what children will
    do, not when, not why, not how.
They do the strangest things, it seems,
It may be to fulfill some extravagant
    dreams.

I'll exemplify what I'm talking about,
So you'll understand without a doubt.
I find it important to share my thoughts
    with you,
So please lend me your ear and be
    attentive too.

When Julie was only two years old,
Of both sides of the toilet bowl she
    took hold.
Down below, the water was a pretty
    blue-green,
Pulled lever makes it twirl where calm
    it was once seen.

It swirled and churned and made a
    funny roar,
Julie seemed bewitched and glued to
    the floor.
She wondered where all this water came
    from and then disappeared out of
    view,
Her experiences with modern plumbing
    were all too few.

Suddenly, thirst took a hold of little
   Julie,
What she did you'll surely agree was
   silly.
Chubby fingers still holding tightly
   at the sides,
Face went forward, head followed,
   and shoulders besides.

Not having extended quite deep enough,
Julie stretched further though it was
    tough.
Success and triumph! Julie finally
    reached the water,
Which enabled her to drink out of this
    household crater.

When I discovered my upside down
    child,
Concerned and revolted, I went wild.
Curly head was nowhere in sight,
Dimply legs kicked with energetic
    might.

The Potty

The urge registers in Nici's young brain,
And to wear diapers she is now too vain.
So she requests the *Potty* and we all
    gladly indulge,
Going to all lengths to avoid that
    dreaded diaper bulge.

On the *Potty* Nici sits till she's fully
    relieved,
Then gets up and inspects what she's
    achieved.
Off to her dresser Nici dashes,
Out of a drawer a fresh diaper flashes.

Clean diaper she neatly spreads,
To the brimming *Potty* decidedly treads.
We watch as the contents get emptied
   onto the diaper,
Stunned, we fail her actions to hamper.

It's been a while since her pants were
   stained,
For Nici is now properly toilet trained.
To empty her *Potty* into the toilet Nici
   still needs to learn,
And that it happens very soon, we
   wholeheartedly yearn.

Standing Up

Wesley is now big enough to do it
   standing up,
Though at first wetting the bowl's rim
   and its top.
He was repeatedly told that he must
   learn to aim,
Much like in any target game.

Wesley finally grasped the manly art,
And was off to a brand new start.
He aimed and shot at everything in
   sight,
At his own toes, flowerpots, and fixtures
   of light.

Things high and low didn't escape his
    notice,
Nothing was immune from target
    practice.
Mom and Dad tried to make Wesley
    quit,
At lengthy lectures the three of them
    would sit.

Practice makes perfect, such no one
    doubts,
But an end must be put to these
    behavioral bouts.
It was unacceptable for Wesley to
    continue his goal,
Drills must be limited to the toilet bowl.

Don't Pee in My Pool

I once saw a poster by a swimming
  pool, on a wall overhead,
"Don't pee in my pool and I won't swim
  in your toilet," it read.
I thought it appropriate because
  everyone knows,
Out of swimmers, urine freely flows.

I don't know when or where that custom
  began,
But it's universally sanctioned amongst
  gentry and hooligan.
In that body of water one can easily
  hide the fact,
Urinating in public with disguised tact.

Those are the habits of mankind which
    I abhor,
They're the reason I stay away from
    pools which I adore.
I squeamishly resist submerging in
    other people's waste,
"Chemicals kill the germs," they'll tell
    me in haste.

Little Sheina is probably the only
    person on earth,
Who emerges from the pool and is
    discerned with mirth.
She pulls hard at the wet suit to abide
    nature's call,
Far away from the water by the garden
    brick wall.

Had this world been blessed with many
more of Sheina's kind,
I'd be diving and swimming with ease
in my mind.
I'd trust that the water which surrounds
my every pore,
Has nothing more unsanitary than
unwashed bodies in store.

Mia

Helpful little Mia offered Mommy
    a hand,
To change her own diaper she thus
    took a stand.
Struggling with the adhesive tab,
Fragile fingers at sticky tape jab.

Finally triumphant and gleefully
    overjoyed,
With the wet diaper Mia trifled and
    toyed.
Exposing her lower half, off the diaper
    came,
Proud and excited Mia became.

To complete her task as Mommy's
   helper,
Into the toilet Mia discarded the
   damper.
Pulling the lever as hard as she could,
To make diaper disappear she thought
   she should.

Watching, Mia still did not get,
Water in the toilet just wouldn't set.
It arose clear out of the repository,
It couldn't pass by the wedged clump
   in that depository.

Linda

Linda wouldn't sit alone on the pot,
Getting bored staying in one spot.
So we allowed her to join us in the
     living-room,
Thinking our company would ward
     off her gloom.

There we all assembled watching
     a television show,
We on the couch, Linda on the potty
     at our feet below.
We sat and watched but to Linda
     were not attentive,
To continue thus sitting she lost her
     incentive.

Off that vessel Linda lifted her bare
  rump,
Damp naked flash that pan wouldn't
  dump.
Centered on our rug, Linda stood in
  a bind,
Gorged potty stubbornly clinging to
  her behind.

Our attention was drawn when hearing
  a heavy thud,
The rug was now mounded with the
  likes of dark mud.
But mud it was not! We realized soon,
As we were sickened and on the verge
  of a swoon.

The pan finally let go of Linda's little
   butt,
It heaped in our living-room in a reeking
   clot.
Linda looked frightened for fear of
   admonishment,
But we were too stunned to think
   of punishment.

Soiled Diapers

I have in the past raised cats and dogs,
My experience even extends to birds
    and frogs.
But most difficult of all is raising
    a child,
In comparison the others were easy
    and mild.

Relief each found in its own unique
    way,
It posed little trouble on any given day.
Cats use their boxes while dogs are
    let out,
Birds and frogs are even easier without
    a doubt.

Now that I'm a Mommy with a child of
   my own,
It's a tiny baby, my precious little Joan.
Experience with animals a hand hasn't
   lent,
I find it difficult though she's Heaven
   sent.

The hardest by far are chores of the
   diaper,
For I've been demoted to a little butt
   wiper.
Diapers need changing around the
   clock,
Night and day, to remove soiled
   diapers I flock.

Once the messy diaper is withdrawn
    in a hurry,
Powder and ointment must be used
    In a scurry.
Can't allow a tiny bottom to get sore,
Against rashes I wage an outright war.

A fresh diaper is in place, now it's time
    for a feeding,
I'm embarrassed to admit that Joan
    lacks breeding.
Minutes into the feast Joan is
    determined to soil,
At a newly filled diaper I once again
    need to toil.

Why couldn't nature equip babies
　　with some sense,
A more reasonable way of their waste
　　to dispense.
I as a Mommy would much rather
　　spend my time,
Playing with my baby than fussing
　　with her grime.

Has a Bark but No Bite

Once Tommy realized it had a bark but
   no bite,
He bravely reached up for its height.
With the help of a stool he grabbed
   and yanked,
Excitedly watching as the water noisily
   cranked.

It swirled and spooled around and
   around,
Flowing in a whirl, downward bound.
With amazement he watched as the
   turbulence stilled,
Slowly and calmly the bowl once again
   filled.

Tommy dropped some paper down
    that well,
Where to it vanished he couldn't tell.
Pulling the lever made the paper flush,
A stormy current took it away in
    a gush.

Tommy cast one object behind another,
All swept with the tide, one after the
    other.
Pulling the lever and watching things
    devoured,
Like magic it all disappeared when
    showered.

Tommy kept feeding this gluttonous
wizard,
Much too gorged, it became a dire
hazard.
It started purging all excess in slow
motion,
There just was no other way, no
remedy nor potion.

The water was overflowing and spilled
to the floor,
It then continued spreading and crept
under the door.
It proceeded through the house, slowly
but surely,
Its surge was seemingly calm but stern
and surly.

A Very Deep Cup

Tamara has recently learned to use
  bathroom fixtures,
The ones that Moms scrub with
  assortment of mixtures.
It hasn't been very long ago at all,
When those utilities were much too tall.

But now that Tamara has grown some,
These are no longer so fearsome.
She gladly mounts when demand
  arises,
Does what she needs then even
  deodorizes.

All would continue good and well,
If not for her older brother, Mel.
Though Tamara's senior, Mel is sadly
    forgetful,
His carelessness is all too shameful.

Out of the bathroom comes Mel,
Leaving behind him a very strong smell.
He also leaves the toilet seat up,
In her turn, Tamara falls into that
    very deep cup.

At School

Rambling Eyes

Teacher scolded and so did Mom and
    Dad,
Thus reprimanded, Jesse felt sad.

They didn't realize that it wasn't his
    fault,
To be so accused was a grave insult.

His eyes wandered onto a neighbor's
    paper, not he,
Couldn't they comprehend it and let
    him be?

He resolved to do his own very best,
Never intended to cheat on that test.

But to control rambling eyes he wasn't
    able,
Though perceiving their behavior
    despicable.

He tried and tried but badly failed,
When the Teacher him thusly assailed.

The New Thermos

Being aware of financial hardships
    in the family,
Acceptance of gifts made Becky feel
    guiltily.
Mom and Dad bought her all that they
    could,
But she was never certain that they
    really should.

In preparation for the first day in
    school,
Mom and Dad got Becky a warm
    sweater of pink wool.
To make her lunches more scrumptious
    and sweet,
They gave Becky a new thermos as a
    special treat.

This thermos was snuggled in a colorful
    lunch-pail,
Ornate with birds, elephants and a blue
    whale.
Becky carried it to school with pride,
Lovingly holding it at her side.

The bell rang to announce recess to all,
Pail and its contents were taken to
    lunch hall.
From its interior Becky carefully
    ejected,
Her special new thermos which she so
    avidly protected.

Soon recess was over, time to go
   back to class,
Becky packed away the thermos and
   into homeroom desired to pass.
Her route was crowded with young
   scholars and much elbowing and
   jolting,
Becky did the best she could though
   at times it was halting.

Suddenly Becky was roughly goaded,
Tumbled on the stairs as her burden
   downward bounded.
She rose to her feet and straightened
   herself out,
Collected her items that scattered all
   about.

While retrieving the lunch-pail, Becky
    heard a jingling sound,
Spying inside, a broken thermos was
    found.
Panicked, to the store Becky hurried,
That her parents hear of the mishap
    she worried.

Intent on exchanging the shattered
    thermos for another,
To stop for advice she didn't bother.
In the store, Becky removed remains
    of the collision,
Swiftly replacing the ruin with a new
    untainted version.

Homeward Becky ambled with downcast
    eyes,
She wasn't proud for living these lies.
At night she was unable to sleep,
And her remorse drove her to weep.

Early next morning to the same store
    Becky dashed,
Back on that shelf the stolen thermos
    she stashed.
She never considered being caught,
Because undoing her crime was her
    only thought.

No one ever found out what Becky had
    done,
But her guilt will never be erased or
    gone.
She won't forget the fear she lived
    through,
And vowed to always remain honest
    and true.

At School ☙ *239*

Where Is Shawn's Shoe?

Shawn is now six and attending first
    grade,
Proudly each morning joins a school-
    bound parade.
Sharp as a whistle and bright as a star,
Such positive attitude will take him far.

One flaw in his character might hold
    Shawn back,
Forgetfulness odds against him will
    stack.
Perhaps not, and I hope I'm wrong,
My convictions may be incorrect though
    very strong.

Shawn might change and take another
    turn,
He's still young and quite likely to learn.
I, his mother, will help him to all ends,
I'll always be supportive, as his ways
    he amends.

Oh, yes! I've forgotten!
I haven't told you how my opinion
    was gotten.
How did I arrrive at the conclusion?
Not, I assure you, from a dilution.

Shawn was marching home from
    school one day,
Periodically stopping to play.
Having little about which to worry,
He wasn't in any kind of a hurry.

Awaiting his entrance through the front
    door,
A long time passed and then even more.
Minutes ticked away rapidly as my
    concern mounted,
Just before my nerves completely failed,
    in Shawn sauntered.

I won't mention his unkempt
    appearance in this narrative,
You won't believe it anyway, of that
    I'm quite positive.
The child looked wild,
Though his disposition remained mild.

One of his shoes was gone,
And I knew not what with it he had
    done.
So I asked, "Where is your shoe and
    sock, as well?"
And he simply replied, "I can't tell."

Maya

This is to those who haven't yet
    experienced the joy,
Of receiving from kindergarten a little
    girl or boy.
Moms and Dads needn't listen for you
    know it well,
You've suffered and tolerated the filth
    and the smell.

You've sent a clean child to school,
Fearing embarrassment and ridicule.
A spotless child leaves home each
    morning,
So people won't be scorning.

Enough said about neatness and such,
All that to Maya doesn't mean very
    much.
As far as she's concerned she could
    never be shamed,
Caring little whether blouse and skirt
    remain tamed.

A tiny pigtail came completely undone,
Several buttons were lost and forever
    gone.
One long sleeve rolled up while the
    other was still down,
Face smudged and resembling a circus
    clown.

Had the disorder and chaos stopped
  right there,
My story wouldn't need to lead you
  elsewhere.
Maya still had one more surprise for
  Mom and Dad,
Bigger and grander than the way
  she was clad.

The following is a continuation of my
  account,
Maya's clothing now lay in a tattered
  mount.
Clouds of dust filled the air,
Heaps of sand dropped on scrubbed
  floor with flair.

Into a bath full of water Maya was
    dunked with a gentle thud,
Clear water immediately turned to dark
    brown mud.
It seemed that she carried home in each
    bodily crevice,
Contents of a sandbox, intending no
    malice.

She was soaked, scrubbed and rinsed
    over and over,
Mom was determined a clean child to
    uncover.
Tomorrow she'll leave home spotlessly
    gleaming,
Mom and Dad will be found once again
    proudly beaming.

New Girl at School

A new girl at school and needing to
    make good impression,
"This school is nice," she makes the
    concession.
Walking down unfamiliar halls,
Making herself at home amongst
    unaccustomed walls.

Ambling and looking every which way,
Sylvie is certain to like it some day.
But for the time being she feels
    lonesome,
And making new friends is so
    cumbersome.

Strolling and gazing here and
  everywhere,
Rewarding her surroundings with
  a glance and a stare.
Wide corridors are covered with cheerful
  decorations,
Giving Sylvie all kinds of exciting
  sensations.

Sylvie takes a detour up one staircase,
Her way back down she's unable to
  trace.
So, down another set of stairs Sylvie
  descends,
Knowing where she's going she all
  along pretends.

But poor Sylvie's foot catches on an
    object unseen,
Landing on the floor, where on her feet
    she had been.
Fearing that others are on the watch,
She quickly stands and snatches her
    fallen bunch.

Oh, no! She realizes that due to the fall,
Her pants split at the inseams and
    reveal all.
A swift mind decides the mishap to
    hide,
Clenching her knees tightly, Sylvie
    waddles from side to side.

Wobbling thusly in a very strange way,
Sylvie manages surprisingly well all day.
Children look sorrowfully at the new
limping girl,
As around her they continually whirl.

She proceeds in this manner of walking,
As a nice boy approaches and wishes to
be talking.
He wants to know whether Sylvie was
born this way,
Leaving her embarrassed and knowing
not what to say.

The Smiths

The Smiths are a fun-loving and
   comical bunch,
They laugh through each meal but most
   of all through lunch.
Jokes fly at the dining table in a scurry,
Each tries to outdo the other in a hurry.

No prank is considered too extreme,
Playfully tricking one another they
   continually scheme.
From the very youngest child to the
   eldest grandfather,
Rare is the occasion when to be serious
   they'd rather.

Teasing and jesting and always in the
  best of spirits,
A hearty chuckle each in turn merits.
Clowning and kidding is the name of
  their game,
Often boisterous and untame.

I was fortunate to witness one of their
  acts,
And shall try to accurately relate the
  facts.
Mom and Dad Smith had a tournament
  while the rest roared with laughter,
Stand by and you too won't suppress
  a cackle hereafter.

I won't go into much detail for I can't
     recall every word,
But I'll reminisce the ending and will
     make sure you have well heard.
What followed in consequence I will
     also convey,
To hear the account you should stay.

The contest between Mom and Dad
     Smith continued for a while,
Both clever in their own individual style.
The end came when Dad Smith lifted
     Mom Smith atop the refrigerator,
From its heights Mom Smith howled
     and awaited
     her liberator.

In class the next morning, Lynne Smith
 made the confession,
She told of her Mom's perch in a *show
 and tell* session.
The kids were impressed and thought
 the narrative hilarious,
Teacher attempted to calm them for
 such stories made her furious.

Mom and Dad Smith heard of Lynne's
 report in class,
They were mildly embarrassed but that
 feeling will pass.
They will continue their games but
 to be discreet proposed,
Hoping that in the future, home
 activities remain undisclosed.

Angry at Teacher

I'm angry at Teacher though I don't
    remember why,
I don't know how to fight back though
    I certainly try.

Teacher is an adult and I'm just a kid,
When I ask for permission she'll
    unreasonably forbid.

I've thought of revenge but never before
    dared,
I guess when I was younger I was still
    scared.

Now that I have grown a couple of days,
I'll carry it out with no further delays.

Next time Teacher hands me a book to
    read,
I'll write on the front cover, "Teacher
    is knock-kneed."

The book will circulate to each
    classmate,
Announcing that Teacher earned
    someone's hate.

They won't know it was me for I won't
    sign my name,
And Teacher won't know whom to
    punish and blame.

Teacher Says Otherwise

Hi, Moms and Dads all over this world,
You, who are daily frazzled and furled.
Your nerves are shattered and stamina
    is low,
You've nearly lost all your youthful
    glow.

I don't wish to discourage and make
    you feel bad,
The last thing I want is to see you look
    sad.
But the truth must be told and that I
    shall do,
To spare assaults on unsuspecting you.

Each stage of your child's life will be
    charged with turmoil,
At which you'll indisputably wince and
    recoil.
Hold on and ride it out as best as you're
    capable,
Escape isn't an option so pray that to
    persist you are able.

Thanks from your children never
    expect,
Don't ever count on their respect.
I seriously doubt their intentions are
    vicious,
They simply won't see your needs or
    your wishes.

To add insult to injury, so to speak,
Unflattering comparisons children will
    sneak.
Most disturbing will be when they
    proclaim,
"Teacher said otherwise," is a statement
    of fame.

The Math Test

"What did you get on your math test,
    Sue?"
Enquiring I witnessed her face blush
    and then turn blue.
She squirmed, fidgeted and scratched
    at her head,
Her young demeanor adopted an
    appearance of dread.

I didn't mean to say anything wrong,
I had no intention her misery to
    prolong.
All I wanted to know was how she did
    on that test,
Expecting only that she's done her
    best.

She continued writhing and stuttered
   a feeble reply,
Shivered and shuddered though it was
   warm mid-July.
"It was Teacher's fault and the whole
   class failed,"
Sue quivered and wailed.

"Teacher doesn't teach and the test
   had trick questions,"
Thus continued Sue with a storm of
   charges and objections.
"Teacher isn't fair and he never
   explained,"
Sue tearfully complained.

This is no coincidence and I heard it
all before,
Nevertheless, such behavior I couldn't
ignore.
Sue was blaming Teacher for her failure
to perform,
"This is unacceptable," I proceeded to
inform.

Had Sue spent more time studying the
material,
She'd have no need to resort to this
raving serial.
It may very well be that Teacher is poor,
But Sue is responsible her own learning
to secure.

I'd gladly offer a tutor had concerns
    been expressed,
She'd get help had I with the need been
    impressed.
But Sue said nothing till this day after
    the examination,
When it's too late to reverse her record's
    contamination.

Out the Window

The third grade class was now fully
    flocked,
Doorway and aisles with kids were
    blocked.
Teacher hadn't entered and the
    classroom boomed,
Free-for-all atmosphere heavily loomed.

With the absence of adult supervision,
Mischief and chaos became a liberal
    provision.
Chairs got overturned while desks
    became dance platforms,
Walls were adorned with graffiti forms.

A heavy pane was unlatched and
    thrown open,
Fresh air into this room didn't flow
    very often.
This portal now became a spacious gap,
An enticement, a risky trap.

Out the open window small items kids
    threw,
Heaps of discards two floors below
    endlessly grew.
Some only stood looking on with
    pleasure,
While others continued tossing with
    no measure.

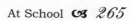

Suddenly the room fell ominously
    hushed,
As through the door Principal rushed.
His hand was caressing a balding
    crown,
While looking left and right and up
    and down.

The kids understood what happened
    right away,
What urged Principal to appear this
    day.
A flying object hit him on the head as
    it fell,
What it was or who did it no one could
tell.

The Waving Hand

In an anxious attempt to always please,
Diana became the perpetual tease.
Eager to show an interest in the subject
  matter,
She asked endless questions, Teacher
  to flatter.

Teacher appreciated her enthusiasm,
But it caused him distressful spasm.
Diana's hand was a permanent fixture
  before his face,
And he vowed the flying appendage to
  efface.

"Stop raising your hand," Teacher told
     Diana one day after class,
The poor girl was about to shatter as
     if made of glass.
How else could she get Teacher's
     attention?
What can she do to sustain his
     retention?

Diana wanted to continually ask,
To make solving problems an easier
     task.
She also loved Teacher, I must stress,
Thus loathed to stop the address.

Teacher told Diana of nightmares
     he's having,
About her hand in the air menacingly
     waving.
He demanded relief of the affliction,
And being freed of her arm's addiction.

Puppy Love

Teachers are potential targets for young
   girls' crushes,
The kind invoking girlish blushes.
The affected girls stutter and babble
   when Teachers query,
Because they're preoccupied with
   needless worry.

Fretting they aren't pretty enough,
That skin is dull and voice too rough.
Brooding about dresses Moms make
   them wear,
Stressing over the color of their own
   hair.

Such has been true through each
   generation,
Girls for teachers have much adoration.
It's never fatal or very long lasting,
But it could definitely be flabbergasting.

The infatuation afflicts unsuspecting
   girls,
Causing head-spins and mind-whirls.
They suddenly lose ability to
   concentrate,
Transforming from mellow to irate.

Each was once an excellent pupil,
Now all efforts seem hopelessly futile.
Homework is prepared but only to
   please,
Tests are taken but no longer with ease.

Just as suddenly as it came,
It'll vanish with no one to blame.
Naive little girls will wake one morning,
Cured of puppy love
   without warning.

Second Floor Window

Audrey played ball in our living
   room setting,
Enough playground space after
   school she wasn't getting.
The ball was being bounced and
   dribbled with might,
Amongst couch, chairs and fixtures
   of light.

It's a wonder that nothing has
   shattered till now,
Such games with the ball I
   begrudgingly allow.
Had she better access to a more
   appropriate place,
Audrey wouldn't need that furniture
   to face.

Audrey continued pouncing and
    skipping,
After the ball she was gleefully
    tripping.
The unruly ball flew straight
    towards the window,
Audrey was right behind it, like
    a faithful shadow.

Out the second floor window the
    two went,
Clear up to the sky my blood
    pressure was sent.
Shrubbery and greens cushioned
    Audrey's fall,
I found her smudged but that
    was all.

The Hall Monitor

Hall Monitors have thankless jobs,
Of dignity and respect the position robs.
It's beyond me and far from the realm
of my imagination,
Why anyone agrees to such
degradation.

Their duty demands policing up and
down halls,
To inspect and investigate behind
secret walls.
To check for culprits in and out of
classrooms,
To search them out on staircases and
in bathrooms.

Coming across this and that offender,
Hall Monitors are required to accost
   till they surrender.
They must report any and all
   infractions,
Whether minor or major attractions.

But the hardest of all their obligations,
Is serving friends with citations.
Best of pals in midst of an offense,
Must be escorted to the Principal at
   any expense.

Their patrols make each a lonely guy,
Because friendship they can no longer
   even buy.
Buddies shy away from them in a snap,
Mistrusting them for fear of a trap.

The Board Monitor

The Board Monitor holds a position
    empowered,
His work isn't hard though boards
    must be scoured.
His pride weapons are mighty and
    fierce,
Any bravado they can easily pierce.

Erasers are the weapons I'm talking
    about,
Being Board Monitor's foe you can do
    without.
If so inclined or ever provoked,
An unforgettable attack may be evoked.

The infamous erasers which the Board
    Monitors use,
Collect chalk-dust while on boards they
    cruise.
All they need is a good shaking,
Shortening breath and rendering eyes
    aching.

Mostly, this dust is pure white,
But sometimes it's colorfully bright.
Board Monitors can also avenge
    Teacher,
For streaks are the eraser's other
    feature.

Teacher's Pet

Jenny is Teacher's Pet this year,
"I have no idea why," she'll swear.
It isn't anything that she savored,
Amongst friends she's no longer
    favored.

A Teacher's Pet has no easy post,
Poor Jenny must endlessly do her most.
Teacher won't excuse a slack of any
    kind,
Putting Teacher's Pet in a major bind.

Jenny's performance must be
    impeccable,
The station she's retaining is
    implacable.
It's exhausting to be good every day,
And irritating in a very
    big way.

To return to friends Jenny is craving,
But to do so she isn't braving.
Teacher will never forgive her for
  quitting,
Thus, Jenny continues miserably
  sitting.

Jenny perseveres at upholding the base,
Though a smile you'll rarely spy on her
  face.
She continues being the Teacher's Pet,
A more unhappy child you've rarely
  met.

Parents Have Forgotten

Parents have plainly forgotten,
That to be good students is darn rotten.
I guess their aging feeble minds,
Can't remember that the gifted are
   always in binds.

In the past they were called *bookworms*,
And were shunned like infectious
   germs.
Today they're spurned and called *nerds*
   and *uncool,*
They're perpetual laughingstocks of the
   entire school.

To add insult to injury, it's often the
   case,
Good students wear glasses on their
   face.
My heart goes out to those poor young
   talents,
Nicknamed *four-eyes* or its equivalents.

Nature dealt them a very raw deal,
Brains are not easy to repeal.
If parents were less selfish about it all,
They'd encourage the gifted their minds
    to stall.

An intellect not used will soon shrivel,
Its owner's life will consequently swivel.
From misfit to well-liked he'll soon turn,
Straight "A" report cards, burn!

A Touch of Excitement

A mind is a terrible thing to waste,
Of math, history and such it should
    get a good taste.
Subjects of learning must be spiced up,
Proper presentation inspiring won't
    stop.

Kids are inherently curious sorts,
Preferring fun because they're such
    good sports.
So, if subjects of learning are made
    more interesting,
For more knowledge kids will inevitably
    be thirsting.

Motivation is the key and must never
    be underestimated,
I guarantee it'll make students
    animated.
A touch of excitement in each learning
    session,
Will avoid the slightest transgression.

Parent-Teacher Night

It was Parent-Teacher Night at school,
Mom and Dad dressed warmly because
    it was cool.
They permitted me to join them but
    outside I'd wait,
Whilst Mom, Dad and Teacher
    discussed my fate.

The three assembled behind closed
    doors,
Impatiently in the hallway I paced the
    floors.
I wasn't anxious for I knew I did well,
But still wished it wouldn't last for
    such a long spell.

Minutes passed and curiosity got the
    better of me,
Peeking through the keyhole there
    was little to see.
Pressing my ear to the door's hard
    wood,
To hear Teacher speaking I now could.

Appalled and disbelieving I heard
    Teacher say,
"Denise is wonderful in every way.
Helpful, bright and cooperative,
Always cheerfully affirmative."

Unable nor willing to listen to one more
   lie,
Pushing at the door into the room I fly.
Looking Teacher square in the eye,
With such whoppers I won't let him by.

"I'm not wonderful in every way!"
Mom and Dad told me so just the
   other day.
"I don't help enough and secrets
   withhold,"
"I don't always listen to what I'm told."

Substitute Teacher

The history teacher stayed out of school
    today,
Students were told that to flu he fell
    prey.
A Substitute Teacher was appointed
    for class,
All were thrilled with anticipation,
    en masse.

On days when Substitute Teacher
    is presiding,
Class fills with merriment and all is
    exciting.
Substitute Teachers are rarely able
    to teach,
Hardly even managing a short speech.

Even kids that don't dare to misbehave,
With Substitute Teachers mischief
    brave.
I've heard of Substitute Teachers being
    outwitted,
Out shouted and to reign not permitted.

At best they need only tolerate flying
    paper,
Optimists among them will admit it's
    a caper.
On days when things really get out of
    hand,
Out of the way Substitute Teacher had
    better stand.

For self protection and basic
    preservation,
To seek shelter they needn't have
    reservation.
Substitute teaching isn't the most
    dangerous of jobs,
But it does rank way up there on
    all my charts.

The School Janitor

The School Janitor is worth a mention
   here,
He's the one with the mop and an
   attentive ear.
He says little but nothing escapes his
   eye,
He silently observes what passes
   him by.

Hushed though he is, one can always
   extract,
A wise word of advice or a reliable fact.
If sincerely shown that a friend is in
   need,
He's always there, ready and willing
   indeed.

Teacher reprimands, Mom and Dad
    punish,
Schoolmates scorn, big brothers
    admonish.
Mankind is against you but not that
    man of silence,
The School Janitor is always there
    to offer condolence.

He'll acquiesce to your requests
    whenever you please,
He willingly cleans up messes on hands
    and knees.
He's always there to offer a comforting
    shoulder,
Being steady and solid as a boulder.

I've seen him mistreated and my heart
   is bleeding,
Mocked and ridiculed, to absurd orders
   heeding.
His pay is low so he dresses in tatters,
And is left out of decision-making on
   important matters.

In spite of it all, he scatters goodwill,
Serenely and efficiently duties will
   fulfill.
He shuffles about with a smile on his
   face,
Body ungainly, soul full of grace.

School Was Discovered

For teaching the three Rs school was
    discovered,
A multitude of mysteries were to be
    uncovered.
Knowledge was sorted by subjects of
    interest,
To satisfy inquisitive minds and settle
    cerebral unrest.

To accurately calculate how many and
    how much,
One must partake in Math, Algebra and
    such.
To unravel the wonders of squares and
    triangles,
Geometry will measure their sides and
    angles.

Geography teaches where events befell,
While when, why and by whom, History
will tell.
Science explains what the others leave
behind,
It's all to open and stimulate a thirsting
mind.

Wisdom of words is found in Philosophy
and Literature,
Physical Education gives bodies
strength and nice curvature.
Economics instructs how to invest,
If accumulation of wealth is the
ultimate quest.

But the most favored and loved on any
  given day,
Are Recess and Lunch, each a
  miniature holiday.
Students and teachers perceive them
  as respites,
Timeouts for refreshment and gathering
  of wits.

Lola and I discussed details on the
  theme,
For such a young child her insight is
  supreme.
She said that Recess and Lunch are
  more important than the rest,
"Because that's when I learn to socialize
  the very best."

Isabel

Isabel likes poetry and sonnets,
That's how she learned about bees and
   bonnets.
Reading enriches her lexicon and bank
   of anecdotes,
Over analogies and prose Isabel
   endlessly dotes.

When classmates complain of a long
   assignment,
At the library, Isabel checks extra books
   out on consignment.
Reading is her greatest pleasure and
   one with which she won't part,
It's a hobby and an all-encompassing
   art.

She began to read at a very young age,
Thirsting for phrases on any size page.
Reading in silence or out loud for an
    audience,
Fluency attests to her experience.

Never does Isabel ignore a written word,
Considers it impossible and totally
    absurd.
Reading billboards, boxes and signs of
    any sort,
She's indiscriminate, unselective and
    doesn't pre-assort.

Thus Isabel accumulated a wealth of
 information,
And is generous and freehanded in its
 application.
Others dislike Teacher and words of
 anger can't stall,
But Isabel says, "She's got a bee in
 her bonnet, that's all."

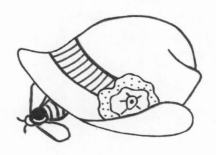

Handful of Worms

We have all experienced and survived
    eccentric teachers,
And wise-guy students in classrooms
    or on field bleachers.
Some teachers are bizarre and
    seemingly proud of that fact,
We've shared classes with pupils who
    dubious attention attract.

I'll now tell you of a science teacher
    I once had,
So weird that I can't decide whether
    funny or sad.
In the same class a few seats away
    from me,
Sat a rascal who just wouldn't let
    things be.

This prankster questioned teacher's
 every move,
To disrupt and attention remove.
Teacher fell prey to each one of his
 frolics,
Being much too naive to fathom his
 diabolics.

Science Teacher attempted to
 demonstrate dissection,
Spilling worms on a tray with care and
 affection.
She grasped a scalpel in one hand,
While around her we all took a stand.

The scamp of the class just couldn't let
    it pass,
Wanting to shame teacher in front of
    the class.
He raised a hand for permission to
    speak,
Feigning innocence, his query sounded
    meek.

"Are these worms edible?" he wished
    to verify,
"They're not poisonous," teacher
    stopped to clarify.
"Can you prove it?" the imp urged,
"Sure!" And a swarm of worms into
    her mouth surged.

The Broken Wrist

It was recess and out to the
   playground we all dashed,
I, amongst my classmates, bumped
   and crashed.
It was my favorite time of the school
   day,
A time to run, shout and play.

We raced and jumped and had
   a wonderful fun,
It was a clear day with a bright,
   warm sun.
Oh! I slipped and as I was falling,
I held out my arm a spill to be
   stalling.

Instantly, sharp pain grasped
    my hand,
It was so bad I could hardly
    withstand.
Looking down where it hurt,
All I saw was a smudge of dirt.

Teachers and kids rushed to see
    what befell me,
Crowding around for a look and
    a see.
To the Nurse's office I was gently
    escorted,
To tend my injury and get the
    confusion sorted.

Nurse determined that my wrist
    was broken,
To Mother on the phone she had
    spoken.
While waiting for Mother to pick
    me up,
Nurse decided that chilling would
    help the pain stop.

Off she went in search of an
    icepack,
But returned with a plastic sack.
The sack contained a quart of
    ice cream,
My favorite, Chocolate Supreme.

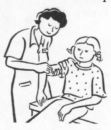

Nurse explained that an icepack
   was nowhere to be found,
But this sack of ice cream was just
   as sound.
In spite of the painful throbbing,
   I desired,
To eat the ice cream when no longer
   required.

Finally and at last Mother arrived,
Of plastic sack and its contents I
   was deprived.
The ice cream needed to be returned
   in a breezer,
For it belonged in the Teachers'
   Lounge freezer.

What I remember mostly about
   that day,
Was the fact that they took the
   ice cream away.
The pain of the broken wrist was
   true and real,
But the shattered dream was a
   bigger deal.

Francy in Kindergarten

In kindergarten Francy was quite
    a handful,
Mischievous, disruptive and fitful.
Teacher tried as hard as she could,
To get our Francy to be good.

Teacher thought it might work,
To improve Francy's conduct with
    a perk.
Rewards were promised for behaving
    well,
But Francy never earned them
    I can tell.

Defeated, Teacher finally became hard,
And told Francy to join her assistant
    out in the yard.
Falsely she thought misbehavior
    aborted,
When from class Francy
    was deported.

Embarrassed and dejected,
Francy wanted this situation corrected.
Tramping back into class, self absolved,
To join her friends Francy resolved.

But Teacher was stubborn and walked
    Francy out again,
Little did she realize that this was
    in vain.
Each time she was taken out of the
    class,
Through the door Francy would once
    again pass.

Teacher finally decided to lock the door,
To assure that Francy would return no
    more.
Surprised and horrified
    Teacher watched,
As through the window
    Francy marched.

Wee Wisdom

5

Trumpets and Clarinets

Aggie woke early before anyone in the
   house,
And rushed to feed her pet mouse.
She was famished herself and listened
   very closely,
"My tummy is growling," she whispered
   hoarsely.

It rumbled like stormy thunder,
That it didn't wake the others was
   a wonder.
While rummaging through the lower
   kitchen cabinets,
Her stomach emulated trumpets and
   clarinets.

Poor Aggie found nothing, for the food
   was kept above,
Though stretching high with an upward
   push and a shove.
Even the chair proved a hopeless resort,
For she was much too short.

Rushing to the refrigerator with
   determination,
Only added to her misery and
   frustration.
She tried and tried with all her might,
But the unyielding door held tight.

Rowdy stomach's clamor reached
   throbbing ears,
Aggie continued hunting in spite of the
   tears.
But suddenly too tired to think,
She settled at the barren table and fell
   asleep in a wink.

All in Knots

Coming home from work all stressed
    and flustered,
After greeting my husband, Margie
    And I closely clustered.
My husband smiled and looked
    concerned,
Gazed into my eyes and agitation
    discerned.

With a weak simper, I asked how their
    day went,
"Mine was awful and I'm totally spent.
My head is throbbing and my inners
    are in knots,
I'm sick to my stomach, my health's
    going to pots."

Heavily sinking into the living room
      couch,
I was cranky and crabby and an awful
      grouch.
There from the sofa, moaning and
      fretting.
I spied little Margie into her room
      trotting.

Soon she returned and gleefully
      bounced,
"I swallowed a hairclip," she proudly
      announced.
All I could do was cry,
While my husband asked, "Why?"

"I didn't want my inners to tangle like
    Mommy's," Margie explained,
"Ooooh!" Exasperated, I complained.
She continued unaffected, "The clip
    will keep everything from dangling,
Like my hair, it will keep it from
    tangling."

Chocolate Is Too Cold

Professionals tell me taste is acquired,
To procure it, time is required.
They say, "Children aren't born favoring
    one food over another,"
But I've seen newborns prefer that
    formula to some other.

Reality contradicts and causes this
    theory to collapse,
If not genetically engineered, then in
    the womb they learned it, perhaps.
From the day of his birth, Larry had
    a preference,
For particular formulas showing more
    reverence.

As Larry grew older and so did his two
    siblings,
They knew what they liked though still
    fledglings.
No matter how hard I tried to dissuade,
Eating what was needed I couldn't
    persuade.

They ate what they liked and refused
    the rest,
All efforts in vain though I attempted
    my best.
Those foods which are nutritionally
    correct,
Are often those to which my children
    object.

Tomatoes have too many seeds while
   bananas are mushy,
Cucumbers are green and mushrooms
   are squashy.
Sandwiches must be stripped of their
   crusts,
Peeling and coring apples are musts.

Fish smells badly while the soup is
   too hot,
Cheese will inevitably go to pot.
Juice is too tangy and peanut butter
   too lumpy,
Chicken is too crispy and dumplings
   are too dumpy.

Yesterday I wanted to treat the kids to
    some ice cream,
And presumed chocolate is what they
    esteem.
But just when I thought I've heard it all,
Larry came up with a new one off the
    wall.

He decided to have vanilla instead,
"Chocolate's too cold and causes an
    ache in my head."
I didn't bother disproving the fact,
So Larry's opinion remained intact.

Raisins in the Bottle

I took Bev to be checked for
    developmental progression,
At the Pediatrician's she made quite
    an impression.
She's just completed two year of age,
And was ahead of herself, very bright
    and sage.

When given various puzzles to
    unscramble,
Bev easily solved them with no lengthy
    preamble.
The pictures she drew were thoroughly
    scrutinized,
Pediatrician was pleased when they
    were analyzed,

Pediatrician, however, was disturbed
    with one test,
And was convinced that Bev had not
    performed her best.
With flying colors Bev passed each and
    every exam,
Why then should this one turn to such
    disgraceful sham?

To check for Bev's hand-eye
    coordination,
Into a tiny bottle she was to make
    a donation.
A raisin was to be dropped through
    its small opening,
But each try left Pediatrician's spirits
    dampening.

Instead of dropping raisins into the
small flask,
Bev took them into her mouth and
failed the task.
The misdemeanor was noted in her
medical chart,
But I was still convinced that Bev
is very smart.

The process was lengthy and her
stomach rumbled,
"Want to eat," she mumbled.
Raisins so tender and sweet,
Were an acceptable treat.

Eating Is a Bore

Payton has never been a good eater,
Always causing hardships to her feeder.
The task was usually her mother's,
But Payton had her druthers.

Food was completely unexciting,
Even ice cream and candy were
    uninviting.
Eating was a waste of time,
Keeping her from play which was prime.

She perceived the task of mastication,
With much disdain and indignation.
While this or that meal Payton fended,
To beloved dolls she could've tended.

But mother had a difference of opinion
    and believed her right,
To force Payton's feeding with earnest
    might.
Thrice or more daily mother put other
    activities on hold,
She and Payton faced one another, both
    stubbornly bold.

Payton felt violated in the crudest way,
She resented being accosted day after
    day.
Why must she be thus required to eat?
It's so very difficult to remain in that
    seat!

To add insult to injury and aggravation,
Mother took Payton to the pediatrician.
Complaining that Payton won't dine,
Doctor examined and found, "She's just
    fine."

Payton needn't consume all that was
    presented,
Requiring only a fraction of what
    mother granted.
As doctor tried to have mother
    convinced,
Payton needn't eat all which she
    evinced.

Payton thrived on minimal nutrition,
Small quantities sufficed for her growth
    and fruition.
Pushing Payton to eat did absolutely
    no good,
It only enhanced her loathing for food.

How to Hold the Bottle

Short on practice and lacking in
   experience,
Young children are blessed with plenty
   of resilience.
I, the grown-up, admit their deeds
   comical,
But to children they obviously seem
   logical.

While I have your attention, please
   allow me a moment,
Humor me and listen to the following
   divulgement.
Baby Bob is my one and only precious
   infant,
Had you met you'd love him in an
   instant.

As with many infants, so with Baby
    Bob,
He doesn't always succeed at his job.
Being so young, his obligations are few,
Among his duties is sucking his brew.

Tiny hands are unable to hold a bottle
    full of food,
So, with his feet Baby Bob holds it
    and good.
I think it much more difficult to do,
But Baby Bob differs and what about
    you?

So what's wrong with this picture and
    what is amiss?
Nothing, I tell you! It's safe to dismiss.
Baby Bob consumes food in his own
    way,
That this is improper, who am I to say?

Christie

Christie is now of that ripe old age,
Prone to frequent tantrums and
    unforeseen rage.
Won't tolerate being fed by someone
    else,
"Me!" She inevitably yells.

The aspiration is certainly sincere,
But lack of coordination with her quest
    interfere.
Hungry mouth is anxious to receive,
But hand and spoon deceive.

En route to the mouth they take a
   detour,
Going for the ear 'cause Christie's aim
   is so poor.
Another attempt still lacks in fruition,
Cheeks splatter but Christie hasn't met
   her ambition.

Not giving up and stubbornly
   unyielding,
All but the mouth fill with fodder while
   Christie's hunger is building.
Ears, nose, eyes and hair,
Are blotted with food as is Christie's
   chair.

Realizing her efforts in vain,
Christie drops the culprit spoon with
disdain.
The rest of the meal will be more of a
success,
As bare hands, into mouth, sustenance
press.

Don't even for a short moment think
and believe,
That eating is now more tidy though
hunger it does relieve.
Christie's face and hair have altered
their original color,
Table and chair are sated with dripping
squalor.

Buy Some Money

I went shopping for provisions, amongst
   them bread and tea,
Four-year-old Nona accompanied me.
She promised to help carry the goods,
Saying she loved shopping for foods.

Off to the grocery we went hand in
   hand,
Taking a detour to a newspaper stand.
The morning paper needed to be
   bought,
To learn the latest and what VIPs
   thought.

We entered the grocery to fulfill a
   mission,
To satisfy our shopping list was the
   proposition.
From a long line of carts we wrenched
   the one on the end,
It wasn't easy but we managed to rend.

Up and down the aisles my little helper
   and I went,
To fill the cart with needed goods was
   our intent.
One after the other we picked essentials
   off shelves,
Accomplishing much and were proud
   of ourselves.

Looking through our list I realized we
   were done,
The selections were ample and more
   items were needed none.
To the checkout we advanced with
   volition,
At the end of a long queue we took our
   position.

To occupy time while awaiting our turn,
I flipped pages of a magazine hoping
    something to learn.
Occasionally I would glance down and
    see,
Nona fingering chocolates with a plea.

She asked me to purchase the sweet,
To satisfy her craving for a sugary treat.
Not wanting to refuse yet disliking her
    eating confection,
I quickly made up an excuse of fiction.

"We haven't enough money," I told her
    shamelessly,
And Nona was saddened obviously.
"Why don't we buy some money?" She
    asked with tearful eyes,
Completely oblivious to
    my blatant lies.

Baby Is Eating Mommy!

Mommy and Daddy, with excitement
and joy,
Brought from the hospital a tiny baby
boy.

Everyone adored Sandy's new baby
brother,
But if she could, she'd trade him for
another.

He cries and howls when Sandy needs
quiet,
He dirties his diapers and causes a riot.

What *broke the camel's back,* so to
    speak,
Was Sandy's witnessing his
    unforgivably mean streak.

She spied Mommy sitting on her bed,
Intending to get baby brother fed.

Sandy saw with horror and understood,
Baby brother eating her Mommy instead
    of food!

Star-Studded Skies

Fear afflicts the young and the old,
Disabling the cowardly and the bold.
It can't be rationalized nor explained
    away lightly,
It won't be ousted not even slightly.

Blake has always been a brave little girl,
Even when Daddy gave the swing a
    strong hurl.
She never showed concern when
    approached by a dog,
She was perfectly calm in the dark and
    the fog.

At amusement parks she shrieked only
    for joy,
Courage and daring were hers to enjoy.
There was, however, one thing that
    Blake feared,
I know not its inception nor
    from where it reared.

It was the oddest thing I've ever
    encountered,
Utterly overwhelming and deeply
    centered.
As Blake laid down for her nightly
    repose,
With anxiety her little body froze.

Blake was afraid of the star-studded
    skies above,
Rejecting the sleep that she would
    otherwise love.
Blinking down at her through the open
    window,
Was this horrifying shadow.

Blake didn't dare give in to slumber,
The sky was huge and stars many
    in number.
Staring up at this monster, Blake
    stayed awake,
Her terrified lookout she wouldn't
    forsake.

Before retiring, Daddy looked in on
    Blake,
In the dark he saw her wide awake.
He entered and drew the curtains
    tightly,
Shutting out all that was scary and
    unsightly.

Daddy earned his heroic good merits,
Reviving Blake's wounded spirits.
Ogre conquered, she was freed to rest,
Her bed was once again a safe nest.

Erica

"You never buy me anything!"
   Proclaimed Erica tearfully,
And continued complaining mournfully.

Last month, for her birthday, I spent
   a bundle of money,
To bestow plenty of gifts upon my child,
   my honey.

Again we went shopping just before the
   school year started,
To acquire for Erica all she needed and
   wanted.

Only last week you could have met
    us on a spree,
Shopping as if we owned a money-
    growing tree.

Today I refused her out of exhaustion
    of resources,
Influenced by frail economic forces.

Erica's memory is extremely weak,
To accuse me as she did was bitterly
    bleak.

I suppose I'm only as good as my
    current benevolence,
The past doesn't credit my bank of
    munificence.

Baby on a Park Bench

Priscilla has been yearning for a baby
    sibling,
One who coos and is from the mouth
    dribbling.
She prefers a sister but a brother will
    do,
Mom will be asked with no further ado.

Mom sends Priscilla to Dad with the
    request,
Perhaps he'll be the one her plea to
    bequest.
Hearing her out, Dad sends Priscilla
    back to Mom,
And thus she is routed to and from.

Mom doesn't refuse, nor does Dad,
But a proper response Priscilla hasn't
    yet had.
Back and forth Priscilla campaigns,
Mom points at Dad while Dad, Mom
    arraigns.

Priscilla fortifies her bid with promises
    to be good,
She'll help with the wash and always
    finish her food.
Priscilla guarantees with infant to help,
By responding to its every crying yelp.

Long time has passed and Priscilla
    finally realized,
Her wish and desire won't be
    materialized.
She was left sad and dejected,
Knowing that her petition was rejected.

Consequently, Priscilla took to daily
    dreaming,
To acquire a baby her mind was
    scheming.
"I'll find a lost baby on a park bench,
    asleep,
And take it home with me forever to
    keep."

Afraid to Sleep

Poor little Ann is afraid to go to sleep,
Though fatigue is mounting in a large
  heap.
Ann struggles to keep her eyes open
  wide,
A broadly gaping yawn trying to hide.

In previous nights Ann repeatedly
  experienced,
Frightening dreams she unwillingly
  audienced.
A big old sorceress was chasing her
  relentlessly,
Items large and small the witch threw
  senselessly.

None of the pitches hit little Ann,
But of such dreams she wasn't a fan.
She tried to escape but remained
  petrified,
Her legs wouldn't move as her fear
  amplified.

The witch never caught her but Ann
  was scared blind,
The memory is still vivid in her terrified
  mind.
Now in her bed, Ann fights off the urge
  to sleep,
Though fatigue is mounting in an ever-
  growing heap.

Sharing Dreams

The best of pals were Dawn and I,
Spending much time conversing eye
    to eye.
We shared many a confidence,
And to find us thus chatting is no
    coincidence.

One morning I related a dream fro
    the night before,
Excited, Dawn wanted to hear more.
My dream was conveyed in colorful
    details,
About puppies and kittens and peacock
    tails.

Done with my narration,
Dawn was aglow with elation.
"My dreams are never so wonderful,"
She was unbegrudging though a bit
    mournful.

She asked to watch a dream with
    me tonight,
When darkness is not disturbed by
    any light.
The best way to view it, or so Dawn
    decided,
"I'll sleep in your bed," and in she
    glided.

It never occurred to Dawn that I can't
    bring dreams up at will,
Allowing her to see my dreams I haven't
    the skill.
Dreams aren't like movies or even TV,
They aren't available for all that wish
    to see.

The Looking Glass

When first discovering the mirror,
Dennis needed assurance that it was
   no error.
He didn't suspect that the image was
   his,
Finding it puzzling and a tempting quiz.

Interest and adventure all drove him to
   test,
This dilemma just wouldn't let him rest.
He checked and inspected every
   possible angle,
It was confusing and his mind was in
   a tangle.

That boy who's confronting Dennis
   so coldly,
Is now echoing Dennis' deeds much
   too boldly.
Making certain and ensuring that he's
   not wrong,
To unravel the mystery Dennis will
   prolong.

Feet wide apart, left arm raised high
   over head,
The reflection mimics but uses the right
   arm instead.
Dennis bounces on one foot with a hand
   at each hip,
The image hops on the other, hands off
   hips never slip.

Now Dennis decides absurd faces to
    make,
Being determined this riddle to break.
Surely, that boy still facing Dennis
    bravely,
Will be caught and embarrassed
    gravely.

He doesn't wish to hurt the other boy's
    feelings,
But Dennis resents his annoying
    dealings.
Dennis is willing to make him a friend,
But this impersonation must instantly
    end.

It won't do to befriend him if he
continues this game,
They look so much alike yet he won't
share his name.
Dennis wants a buddy with whom he
can play,
But one who will have things of his
own to say.

Cousin Amos

Oddly professional and businesslike,
Cousin Amos was teaching me to
   ride a bike.

"You're not too bad," Amos
   conceded,
As my afternoon lessons proceeded.

It seemed easy as long as he ran
   close behind,
His presence gave me confidence
   and peace of mind.

After several lessons I did extremely
   well,
Picked up my speed and never fell.

And today Amos ran behind me
  as he did the day before,
While my skill increased and my
  speed even more.

But suddenly, from a distance
  I judged much too great,
Amos warned, "Watch how you
  navigate!"

I began wobbling and my heart
  throbbed with fear,
Because Amos, my mentor, was
  no longer near.

To assess the distance between
    Amos and this runaway vehicle,
I turned but soon realized this move
    was too radical.

The two-wheeler upon which I was
    astride,
Face forward into a thorny rosebush
    took me for a ride.

Milk Is White

Children ask the most baffling
  questions,
I have no idea where they get their
  selections.
Often times these are so perplexing,
Forcing adult brains to be bending
  and flexing.

"Where do cows get their milk?" Kelly
  asked at the breakfast table,
But to answer her intelligently I wasn't
  able.
Knowing little of such a matter,
I became uncomfortable with the
  chatter.

I should have admitted my shortage
    of knowledge,
But to appear unwise before my child
    I lacked courage.
I snapped a quick reply in Kelly's
    direction,
Praying that no one witnesses my
    infraction.

"Cows eat lots and lots of grass,"
I hoped Kelly will let it pass.
She could have been appeased with
    how I retorted,
Instead, to further interrogation
    she resorted.

"But grass is green and milk is white,"
Kelly insisted, oblivious to my plight.
Such data my brain did not include,
And I no longer wished my child to
    delude.

Persistent quizzing I pretended not to
    hear,
Her attention I managed in different
    direction to steer.
Years have passed since and I still
    don't have the correct reply,
And to be honest, I don't even try.

Pictures in the Night

Through the window, two young girls
    beheld a brilliant light,
Its radiance was so great that they
    startled at its sight.
It was late and past nightfall, the young
    girls knew,
But this bright light illuminated as the
    sun can only do.

Having witnessed the likes for the very
    first time,
They were much too excited for sleep,
    so into beds didn't climb.
They knew not what to make of this
    vision of lustrous splendor,
So, at the window remained to await the
    next sky-splitting bender.

An additional shiner amazed the young
    girls afresh,
It filled them with delirium and prickled
    their flesh.
It was dazzling and resplendent and
    bigger than life,
The young girls pondered, their minds
    all astrife.

Thinking led them down memory's very
    brink,
"When Daddy takes pictures the flash
    makes us blink."
So that's what this must have been
    without a doubt,
Someone was taking pictures all about.

It certainly was an enormous camera
  that was being used,
"This is much bigger than Daddy's
  flash," they mused.
But why were so many photos being
  taken so late after dusk?
In the darkness, amidst flowers and
  trees and their musk?

I've nearly forgotten to relate a detail
  of importance,
Lacking this trivia won't minister your
  cognizance.
That light was closely followed by
  rumbling thunder,
For this was a storm which the girls
  were under.

Eyeglasses

As soon as it was discovered that his
   eyesight was blurry,
Spectacles were prescribed in a hurry.
Now young Robert wears corrective lens,
Impaired vision to enhance.

Large frames on a narrow nose ride,
A major part of his face they eternally
   hide.
Their structure is dark while lenses are
   clear,
Robert guards them, realizing they are
   dear.

Strangely enough, Robert loves wearing
   his glasses,
They get him out of fist fights and all
   kinds of messes.
He diligently cleans them when noticing
   a smudge,
Off his face they rarely budge.

He refuses to part with them even for
　　sleep,
When asked to remove, he insists them
　　to keep.
He professes that without them each
　　dream is unclear,
Incomprehensible and a blurry smear.

Mom and Dad yield to Robert though
　　they deem him foolish,
Over such trivia they won't be bullish.
Each morning Robert relates the
　　wonderful dreams he's seen,
Thanking his beloved glasses for
　　through the night on his nose
　　they've been.

They Get Injected

An age-old question and the one
   children frequently ask,
"Where do babies come from?" giving
   parents quite a task.
For some odd reason at which I dare
   not guess,
Parents are intimidated when for reply
   children press.

You'd think that parents have matured,
Shed their shyness and insight
   procured.
But this question causes so much
   distress,
Parents recoil and remain silenced by
   stress.

So children make up stories when facts
    are not furnished,
Though crudely unrefined and needing
    to be varnished.
We must forgive these blameless lies,
Which to true facts have little ties.

Where do babies come from is simply
    deduced,
A fable has just been introduced.
A myth is mistaken for a fact,
Falsely, mystery solved and intact.

When for new baby Mom and Dad
     crave,
They march to the doctor, courageous
     and brave.
An injection each gets in turn,
They fear it not though it may burn.

One sort for a girl and another for a
     boy,
It all depends on their fancy and what
     they'd enjoy.
The appropriate needle is selectively
     inserted,
To parents they'll soon be converted.

A Peculiar Fellow

There is something strange pursuing
   Andy,
At times it's smooth, at others coarse
   and sandy.
Changing direction that Andy is facing,
Now it leads and Andy is racing.

Sometimes it appears short and
   stumpy,
Other times rounded and humpy.
Unpredictably tall as a tree,
Or narrow and straight as can be.

It perpetually appends to some part
   of Andy's body,
One might presume it in Andy's
   custody.
But Andy wants little to do with this
   thing,
Yet it continues to cling and cling and
   cling.

In reality, it isn't all that bad,
For it could be the pal that Andy's never
    had.
It never argues nor asserts a claim,
It goes where Andy wishes, silent and
    tame.

Allow me your questions to relieve,
Andy didn't comprehend but you should
    I believe.
What Andy discovered is simply a
    shadow,
And discerned it a very peculiar fellow.

Heather

A favored game among children at play,
Is *let's pretend* all day.
They never tire of simulating,
Fantasizing and emulating.

That's part of growing up,
It's healthy and need not stop.
Imagination will mature into creativity,
Ripen to a constructively building
    activity.

Heather's hair was always cut short
    about her head,
Monthly trips to the hairdresser she'd
    plainly dread.
Mommy believes short hair is more
    practical,
But Heather thinks that it
    looks comical.

Heather dreams of long locks on her
    head,
Pretending, she ties scarves instead.
It's of one sort or another,
Attaching one after the other.

Now she's endowed with a flowing tail,
Multicolored tresses behind her trail.
Heather loves it without a doubt,
Now possessing the long hair she's been
    dreaming about.

In front of a mirror Heather turns from
    side to side,
Admiring her reflection and delight
    doesn't hide.
She's proud of her creative deed,
Because she looks great with long hair,
    indeed.

Sweaters in the Heat

If you think that Mary is quite contrary,
Wait and see how our Renee can get.
She disputes every point beyond
  boundary,
Against all that she's told her mind
  will set.

When the world uses warm clothing
  from cold to protect,
Renee insists that summer dresses
  and sandals she'll wear.
Summertime and scorching heat,
  sweaters Renee will collect,
For she'll don that which all winter
  she wouldn't bear.

Mom and Dad remain muted,
Disputing Renee they feel beat.
Her thinking won't be refuted,
The harder they try the more
    apparent their defeat.

So our adverse little lady,
Continues to do as she pleases.
Mom and Dad pray she's soon cured
    of her malady,
And life for them eases.

Small World

Think back, adults, to those long ago
  days when you were small,
When everything seemed so very, very
  tall.
Things that now seem of reasonable
  height,
Once appeared to have so much might.

Brenda is now four years of age,
Bright, energetic and, at times, even
  sage.
She and Grandma walked up a hill,
Occasionally looked down with thrill.

Their eyes observed incredible scenery,
More stunning than pictures at an art
  gallery.
Houses, trees, blue skies and a flat
  green field,
Sparkling and glowing,
  to the sun all yield.

Most impressive to Brenda was a little
    church,
For its towers and crosses providing
    a perch.
It seemed of just the right size,
Perfectly beautiful to her young eyes.

Brenda insisted going this day,
To the little church across the bay.
She's been wanting a new dollhouse
    but this will do well,
And was even hoping that it's got
    a small bell.

Grandma pondered in confusion,
"How do I make Brenda realize that
    this is only an optical illusion?"
She worried about Brenda's
    disappointment today,
When they encounter the very big
    church across the bay.

What Is Rain?

Children make up stories about things
    they don't understand,
I wish to convey one in particular, so
    your ear I demand.

What makes the rain fall Derek didn't
    comprehend,
And needed to bring this mystery to a
    satisfactory end.

Collecting bits and pieces that crossed
    his mind,
Derek came up with a theory of some
    kind.

"Rain is God's tears," Derek declared,
And this dilemma was
    properly squared.

Rickie and Mickie

Rickie was a curious child,
Rambunctious, naughty and wild.

All his waking time was busily spent,
On exposing novelties perpetually bent.

Fingering unfamiliars in his route,
Hungering to figure them all out.

Big rounded eyes eternally open wide,
Nothing from his sight could easily hide.

Last week, I remember quite clear,
Rickie's behavior filled me with fear.

As we walked down a city block,
It must have been twelve or one
   o'clock.

A man with a long flowing scarf and
    nose like a hawk,
Briskly tried to pass us on the sidewalk.

That he was a stranger was plain to see,
But Rickie just couldn't let him be.

He grabbed at the scarf and wouldn't
    let go,
Because this person he wanted to know.

The stranger bent low and widely
    beamed,
While my heart stopped and I almost
    screamed.

When they swapped names and shook
   hands,
Rickie and the stranger became instant
   friends.

Pals and buddies are my young Rickie,
And this stranger who called himself
   Mickie.

Flooded Basement

Daddy tinkered with pipes in the
   basement causing a flood,
The downpour was severe enough
   to chill his blood.
Danger of grave damage heavily
   loomed in the air,
Daddy's concern mounted and
   stress was now bare.

He tried to repair while wading in
   two feet of water,
But hadn't a clue as to what was
   the matter.
To avoid further harm the source
   must be severed,
Thus Daddy deftly endeavored.

He worked and labored all evening
   long,
Trying to correct that which has
   gone wrong.
Tired hands dropped the flashlight,
   leaving him in the dark,
But not before his efforts made a
   significant mark.

Along came little Laurie, tears
   rolling down a pudgy cheek,
Voice quivered as she tried to speak.
"There is no water in the house,"
   she finally blurted out,
And sank into yet another crying
   bout.

"The water had to be turned off
    because I made a mistake,"
Daddy admitted with an ache.
"I've got it under control but you
    should be sleeping,"
Daddy squatted down while Laurie
    continued her weeping.

She wouldn't be consoled nor listen
    to Daddy's assurance,
It was all too hard for her youthful
    endurance.
"I wanted to wash my baby dolls,"
    she persistently wailed,
Turning an angry shoulder, away
    Daddy's five-year-old sailed.

The Injection

Mom took Drake to the Pediatrician,
A famous children's physician.
It was time for Drake's booster
    injection,
He took the news with utter
    dejection.

Highly disliking to be jabbed in such
    a way,
Drake decided to speak up this day.
He will no longer put up with the
    abuse,
To be thus poked he'll flatly refuse.

In Pediatrician's office they
   anxiously waited,
To put Drake through such stress
   Mom truly hated.
There was really no choice or a way
   out,
Drake needed his inoculation
   without a doubt.

Pediatrician had Mom roll up a
   sleeve,
To expose Drake's arm and be ready
   to receive.
The appendage was ready but Drake
   was not,
This affair was unfair and despised
   a whole lot.

Fear and disdain were replaced by
  courage,
Drake was prepared to express his
  outrage.
Moments before the needle pierced
  his skin,
Into Pediatrician's eyes he looked
  with a grin.

The moment was still and
  unbearably intense,
"I've seen men hang for a lesser
  offense!"
So Drake stated and so heard Mom
  and Pediatrician,
As the needle penetrated with
  painful volition.

The Funny Bone

Maggie saw Mom's face pale and
   turn to stone,
When banging that spot which is
   called the *Funny Bone*.
Funny it isn't, as Maggie well
   knows,
Having experienced it in her own
   elbows.

A less appropriate name could not
   have been given,
The *Funny Bone* isn't at all funny,
   not ever nor even!
Thumping it in a particular way,
Could ruin anyone's day.

Maggie wishes she was older,
More influential and bolder.
She'd insist on changing that silly
　　name,
Funny Bone is so absurdly lame.

Rechristen she would that part of
　　the arm,
The one which so frequently comes
　　to harm.
Named it shall be the *Shocking
　　Joint,*
For it definitely knows how to make
　　a point.

The very next time her elbow was
    batted,
At the sore spot Maggie mournfully
    patted.
"My *Shocking Joint* broke!"
Maggie sniffled and tearfully spoke.

Defective Baby

A new-born baby was brought into
  the house,
Little Gina thought it scrawny and
  looking like a mouse.

The idea of sharing Mom and Dad
  was strongly spurned,
While she petitioned for new-born
  baby to be returned.

He's defective and below minimum
  standards,
His flaws are obvious from inside
  outwards.

New-born baby cries when laid to
  sleep,
Yet Mom and Dad
  propose him to keep!

He leaks in his diapers and dribbles
    at the mouth,
He's heard in the north part of the
    house and the south.

Even his hands don't work as they
    should,
To eat by himself you'd expect that
    he could.

Mom and Dad are seemingly devout,
Though he's broken and damaged
    without a doubt.

He must be returned from where he
    was taken,
Before the warranty runs out and
    all hope is forsaken.

Mommy's Flower Garden

Flowers expire when cut and the
  thought brings on a flow of tears,
Rosie is convinced for witnessing it
  for years.

She watches as to the flower garden
  Mommy strides,
To snip roses in which she so much
  prides.

Mommy arranges doomed flowers in
  a vase,
Which stands ornately on a starched
  doily of lace.

It is obvious to Rosie and clear as
  a bell,
In the vase, flowers will
  never fare well.

It takes but a day or two at best,
For beautiful flowers to lose vigor
   and zest.

Soon they will wilt and die,
Glorious heads on a weak stem
   will lie.

Mommy won ribbons for her garden
   of flowers,
Friends bestow complimentary
   showers.

But Rosie wishes she could speak
   out on this grave matter,
"Mommy's misdemeanor doesn't
   warrant positive flatter!"

Battle Scars

Cameron loves flaunting a scar or
    a bandage,
Whether it be on the face or an
    appendage.
The bigger the better and bearing
    more charm,
Young audience is drawn to assess
    the harm.

Friends don't begrudge his treasure,
Displaying contusions is an
    undeniable pleasure.
Each youngster in turn shows off
    the same,
It seems to be such a fashionable
    game.

They "ooh" and "ah" at each
   marvelous vision,
Surely it was earned on a heroic
   mission.
Proudly Cameron tells an
   extraordinary fable,
Involving a skirmish with a chair
   and the dining-room table.

They all want to know how this
   bandage was gotten,
Absorbing details never to be
   forgotten.
When their turns come to show
   off badges of courage,
They'll relate their own tales of
   horror and outrage.

The contest is on as they try to
  outdo one another,
Competitors come up with incredible
  dressings one after the other.
Respectful young adversaries
  observe and hear,
While each poses with his own
  awesome gear.

Baby Discovers Toes

Tiny infant, newly born,
Dearly loved yet seemingly forlorn.

To discover the world she'll strive,
Exploring the novelty — "I am alive!"

Stretching out a miniature hand,
Reaching for a universe so grand.

Behold! Revelation! Her toes are
    discovered,
Chubby and wiggly when bare and
    uncovered.

Baby didn't conceive or reason,
Suspected no betrayal or treason.

Into toothless mouth toes were
    received,
To taste oddities not yet fully
    perceived.

Surprisingly powerful jaws clamped
    on a teensy toe,
Baby's own mouth became a
    villainous foe.

Sore and hurt and throbbing with
    pain,
Baby shrieked in angry disdain.

To sooth her baby, Mommy came
    near,
Lovingly smiled at her
    poor silly dear.

Mom Wisdom

Not Fair

It isn't fair, it isn't just,
To behave mature I'm told I must.
But I still like to play and act bratty
    as can be,
I'm not fully grown as you can well see.

Just because I'm forty and a mother at
    that,
I'm expected to be adult at the drop of
    a hat.
A parent I am, I don't plan to deny so,
But my pranks will continue, you also
    should know.

Mom Wisdom ☞ 3.9.9

Larks and mischief are what I'm all
 about,
Regardless of my age I won't cast them
 out.
Being grown-up is boring and totally
 unappealing,
Youthfulness, however, is enticingly
 healing.

I insistently play ball and hug my teddy
 bear,
I won't avoid puddles nor cut my hair.
I refuse watching news when cartoons
 are available,
I shy away from big words of multi-
 syllable.

I adore doing puzzles or a coloring book,
Through kaleidoscopes I prolong a
    second look.
To the floor I'll drop to partake in a
    game,
Alongside my children marbles I'll aim.

I provide well for my kids, as all
    mothers should,
And at my executive position I am truly
    good.
But the moment I'm done with the adult
    obligation,
I'll join a contest of miniature-boat
    navigation.

As you can see, it isn't at all forthright,
To continue as I am is my constitutional
    right.
I shouldn't be sneered at nor scoffed in
    disdain,
Forgive my adolescence and adulthood
    I'll gladly sustain.

Why?

An infuriating phase in your child's life,
Is while everything to him is a wondrous
strife.
Curiosity gets the better of your kid and
his intentions,
When he yearns to straighten and
explain any and all contentions.

The devices he uses to achieve his
goals,
Are not hammers nor chisels nor poles.
Children were granted the abilities to
ask,
And they rarely let it waste or abandon
the task.

Because it's so difficult to understand,
Toddlers need your supporting hand.
It won't be easy to patiently stand by,
While your tykes continue asking,
"Why?"

"Why is the moon round tonight when
   last week it was not?"
"Why must I sleep when I want to play?"
   and "Why is the sun so hot?"
"Why is Mommy's face smooth while
   Daddy's prickles?"
"Why touching my toes sometimes
   tickles?"'

When asked to clean his mess, Johnny
   wants to know, "Why?"
But "Why" does Johnny's nose run
   when he's had a good cry?
Johnny must finish his apple "But why
   not when dinner is served?"
Johnny's asked to draw a straight line
   but "Why not curved?"

Siblings Fight

Parents, don't interfere when your
  children fight,
Stay away, keep quiet and get out
  of sight!

Spats between siblings are easily
  resolved,
Without outside forces they'll soon
  be dissolved.

How can I stress the point to its most
  extreme?
Parents, butt out! Regardless of the
  theme.

Quarrels are quickly abated and settled,
But only if you, Parents, haven't
  meddled.

My Dad Is Better

Oh, how they swagger and boast,
Flaunt their Moms, but Dads the most.
"My Dad is bigger," regardless of his
    size,
"Mine is smarter," to out brag each
    child tries.

It's a contest of utmost importance,
At all time and under any circumstance.
It's a tournament of perseverance,
One of patience and endurance.

Consider competitions where victory
    doesn't prevail,
Conquest and triumph need not for
    long hail.
Today Charlie scored the most points,
Tomorrow it'll be Josh whom the world
    anoints.

This match has no winners thus
   produces no losers,
It's simply a game of earnest amusers.
It makes no difference who is right or
   otherwise,
No one cares whether the assertions
   are true or lies.

Woe is he who has no Mom or Dad
   to speak about,
Amongst luckier friends he must go
   without.
He has no one about whom to rave
   and brag,
Pity and shame, it's like having no tail
   to wag.

Our Child

Long time ago and very far away,
I remember it vividly though on a
    distant day.
A very loving couple were my Mom
    and Dad,
Adoring me whether I was good or bad.

But when I was naughty, or so they
    thought,
Because I ignored what they had
    taught,
They were driven by anger and
    frustration,
And allied against me in cooperation.

They'd sit on the couch in the family
    room,
Discussing and planning my very doom.
Your Child was tossed between my
    father and mother,
As I witnessed being surrendered from
    one to the other.

My memory doesn't fail me when
    recalling better times,
When Mom and Dad weren't angry for
    I committed no crimes.
When they met in the family room for
    all to see,
My Child was what each possessively
    called me.

Please make up your minds once and
    for all,
Am I forever to be tossed like a
    bouncing ball?
As your child I would much rather
    be shared,
So, call me *Our Child* and have my
    feelings spared.

Better yet, Mom and Dad, call me
    by my name,
The one you gave me when into the
    world I came.
My Child and *Your Child* doesn't do
    any good,
I've got a name, so use it you should.

I Don't Know

Now that Todd has grown a bit,
To ask "why" is no longer fit.
It's become your turn, Parents, to ask
    "why,"
To understand the child you'll endlessly
    try.

It won't be any easier so don't relax yet,
Because disheartened you'll once again
    get.
For instance ask Todd, "Why are you
    late?"
"I don't know," he'll explicitly state.

To stress the drama and emphasize
    it pointedly,
Both shoulders rise and fall jointly.
Because it's unclear whether he truly
    doesn't know,
Parental frustrations will continually
    grow.

With all those "whys" that Todd got
    answered in the past,
You'd think that some of the knowledge
    would somehow last.
The roles have reversed and Parents
    ask "why,"
But to answer, Todd doesn't even seem
    to try.

Three Is a Crowd

I'll tell you about Jean, knowing she's
    not unique,
Such youthful behavior is universally
    antique.
Two is company while three is a crowd,
Her conduct is nothing about which to
    be proud.

Though Jean's demeanor is mostly
    amiable,
Concurrently to handle two friends she
    isn't able.
When three come together attempting
    to play,
The weaker among them won't for long
    stay.

Two out of three in every combination,
Will contrive and conspire till one's
    termination.
Three is an odd number, we all know
    very well,
Jean and her friends make that clear
    as a bell.

Hug Your Children

Listen, parents, and learn from a
    mistake I've made,
Someday this lesson will come to your
    aid.
My little Kevin — cuddly, bouncy and
    playful,
I lovingly nibbled at him by the
    mouthful.

Kevin, through no fault of his own,
Learned that biting is an acceptable
    known.
Being so small and youthfully
    impressionable,
He bites what he likes, guilelessly
    insensible.

When he attempted to sink his teeth
    into me,
I aborted clamped jaws, laughing with
    glee.
My error was realized when a week ago
    or more,
Into a neighboring baby's eye two front
    teeth Kevin bore.

My heart stilled and blood in my veins
    turned to frost,
I was certain that baby's eye was lost.
But thankfully, fortune was on our side,
The wound wasn't serious though quite
    wide.

The moral of my story is here before
    you,
I have no doubt that you got it too.
Cuddle and hug, kiss and pat all day,
But never ever bite, even in play!

Horseback Riding

Leah and Sarah asked to be taken
　　horseback riding,
I gave in to their pleas by
　　begrudgingly abiding.

Leah sat on the saddle stiffened
　　with terror,
Complying with their wishes was
　　probably an error.

Not knowing how that beast to steer,
Sarah's eyes radiated unmistakable
　　fear.

The adventure started with second
　　thoughts in our hearts,
Moving with caution as should be
　　done with all starts.

Leah and Sarah proceeded ahead,
I, close behind, watching with
   dread.

Leah and Sarah were sturdy but
   may be unfurled,
Dwarfed by these animals, I feared
   they'd be hurled.

Leah's horse cooperated and on the
   path stayed,
Sarah's, unmindfully, into the
   woods strayed.

Leah concentrated and tightly
   reined,
Panicked Sarah at her runaway
   mount shrilly complained.

I must make a decision but I don't
    know how,
I must make up my mind in a hurry
    somehow.

Shall I stay with Leah to assure that
    on the path she and her horse
    stay?
Or do I follow Sarah into the woods
    and stop them from further to
    stray?

I'm only one mother who must
   protect the two,
How to accomplish that feat I had
   no clue.

So I yelled as loudly as I could,
For someone to help us if they
   would.

Along came a gentleman of obvious
   good breed,
Gallantly saved us — the three
   maidens in need.

To Err Is Human

I believe that to err is human,
Among every man and every woman.
The mature among us will never hide,
When finding ourselves on error's side.

Erring can be a learning experience,
Though at times an inconvenience.
One must daily amend mistakes made,
And never defer and allow them to fade.

Those who claim they never blunder,
Are precisely the ones that will soon
    go under.
They are the ones who either do not
    a thing,
Or deny their falters and thus learn
    nothing.

It isn't only children who fear
    acknowledging a mistake,
Immature of all ages will go to lengths
    innocence to fake.
One mustn't blame youth for resorting
    to fabrication,
'Cause they're only mimicking their
    elders' vindication.

The Bogeyman

Your child misbehaves and you
    threaten, "The Bogeyman will get
    you now,"
Not specifying who that might be, nor
    when, nor where, nor how.
Your child goes about his business,
    suspiciously looking around,
All senses on alert, for the Bogeyman
    to be found.

He's fearful of the Bogeyman, as of
    any unknown,
And it isn't only because he's not yet
    grown.
It's natural to suspect that which is
    mysterious,
At the same time be inquisitive and
    eagerly curious.

On the one hand, he wants to meet the
    Bogeyman with all his heart,
On the other, he's apprehensive of what
    will happen from the start.
The Bogeyman may hurt him in some
    disastrous way,
He queries friends and relatives but
    none can say.

Now look what you've accomplished
    and what he's become,
You've transformed him from confident
    to worrisome.
Energy is spent looking for the
    Bogeyman he dreads,
Anxiety is apparent as apprehension
    spreads.

Your child's behavior hasn't improved
  any,
Pranks and mischief are still many.
For the Bogeyman he's perpetually
  looking,
Bogeyman's existence is forever
  spooking.

Your Child Is Crying

Your child cries seemingly in pain,
You'd like to ignore it but the noise
    drives you insane.
Your gut tells you that not much is the
    matter,
But your heart won't stop anxiously
    going pitter-patter.

What if you're wrong? What if you're
    mistaken?
And you know that his needs must
    never be forsaken.
You look him over and thoroughly
    inspect,
Each imperfection you question and
    suspect.

The child isn't hurt, you're fully
    convinced,
Close scrutiny has doubtlessly evinced.
But he's still crying and your heart is
    breaking,
The pain may be real yet he may also
    be faking.

Better safe than sorry, I always say,
Take him to the Doctor this very day.
Doctor may confirm the initial
    suspicion,
Relieving you of guilt and inevitable
    contrition.

Don't make decisions you may regret,
It's perfectly natural over your child to
    fret.
Take his crying as seriously as you may,
Don't postpone Doctor for another day.

A Bundle of Peril

Teddy my child, you bundle of peril,
On Monday you nearly drowned in
   a water-filled barrel.
On Tuesday you tried to fly like an
   aircraft,
On Wednesday the sheriff dug you
   out of a shaft.

In the past you've done many
   hazardous deeds,
Recalling them my heart once again
   bleeds.
Your wounds were never a
   deterrence,
You abused yourself
   with irreverence.

I can't stop caring or look away
    unseeing,
My fear for your safety overwhelms
    my whole being.
I don't enjoy fretting and by nature
    I'm not a fusser,
It's just that you're such a frightful
    musser.

The ultimate happened just this
    afternoon,
I guess you were reaching for the
    stars and the moon.
You climbed on the roof and fell
    off on your head,
I was certain that this time was
    the ultimate end.

I'm forever thankful to God above,
He must be watching over you,
    my love.
If that weren't true you'd long be
    gone,
Too much injustice to your body
    you've done.

Age Discrimination

The following is my formal protest,
And I dare you to contest.
This is a pure and simple case of age
    discrimination,
You'll surely agree when you hear my
    explanation.

A yearling's first steps boggle everyone's
    mind,
Though he wobbles and falters and
    lands on his hind.
He's watched with adoration because
    he's cute when going *plunk*,
If I did the same I'd be mistaken for
    a drunk.

The first words a child utters are
    unclear and distorted,
Chuckles of pleasure at such cleverness
    are never aborted.
But if on occasion I slur a word or two,
They call "stupid" or "crazy," you know
    who.

Hands above the head and clapping
    one, two, three,
Will spark comments of appreciation
    and glee.
I'll bet if I mimic and am observed,
A gale of boos and hisses will be served.

Now do you appreciate the point I'm
    making?
To the Supreme Court this case I'll
    be taking.
Such unfairness must instantly be
    stopped,
This kind of injustice needs to be
    cropped.

To retract my charges I'll need an
    apology,
Sincere and in favor of my ideology.
I must have a promise that it won't
    happen again,
Convince me that my efforts weren't
    in vain.

Minnie Versus Mickey

In search of a new family car,
Parents looked through consumer
  reports for this year's star.
All indications pointed to a particular
  mini-van,
And they shared their decision with
  little Dan.

Hearing the news and to Parents'
  irritation,
Dan broke out into a lengthy
  lamentation.
"What is the problem? Why are you
  crying?"
To which he responded, "I don't like
  what you're buying!"

The wailing continued and Parents
    still had no clue,
Why was Dan so miserably blue.
"I don't want a *Minnie*-van," Dan's
    disclosure started,
"I want a *Mickey*-van," the child
    imparted.

Be explicit, be concise,
Don't allow language to thus surprise.
Save yourselves the trouble and
    grievance too,
Don't presume that children correctly
    interpret you.

The above was a perfect example of
    misunderstanding,
And I hope that communication you'll
    succeed amending.
You were surely amused by this little
    tale,
But my intention was to hit you
    proverbially on the nail.

436 ᘒ Bless the Children

No, No, No!

Let me convey the phase of all stages,
About which I could easily fill many
  pages.
But I won't take up too much of your
  time,
And it won't even cost you, not a dime.

Brady was two when he first began
  speaking,
Words and short phrases out of him
  started leaking.
He chattered and prattled through each
  wakeful hour,
Amazing to see a tiny mouth with so
  much power.

He acquired enough words to rave
    about,
But "No" was his favorite, without
    a doubt.
"No" is short and easily pronounced,
Many times daily Brady had it
    announced.

"No" to directions from Mom and Dad,
"No" to his peers and the latest fad.
"No" to big brother when suggesting
    a game,
'No' all day, to whatever came.

Dramatically, one shoulder twitched up,
I didn't even bother getting him to stop.
For I knew that he'd outgrow this
    affliction on his own,
Meanwhile I indulged in an occasional
    groan.

I Was Raised This Way

A kid's classic apology and one which
    will surely ruin your day,
Is when he tells you, "I'm sorry, but I
    was raised this way."
Don't take it to heart and don't feel so
    badly,
Though he probably meant it, I must
    admit sadly.

The media is great about siding with
    kids,
But their hype is a bunch of misdeeds.
I'll be the first to admit when I'm wrong,
But must it be broadcasted with dance
    and song?

Some kids need protection from
    righteous associations,
But many have terribly negative
    affiliations.
Most parents mean well though don't
    always succeed,
To view them as kids' foes is a folly,
    indeed.

Kids are rightly encouraged and
    empowered,
While their parents are unfairly
    showered.
Moms and Dads are perpetually and
    forever blamed,
Thus their kids are convinced and
    inflamed.

It Does Not!

Beware and be forewarned, parents
    out there,
Before finding yourselves in an
    unpleasant affair.

If you've spent twelve ninety eight on
    cream for your face,
Don't declare it costs thirteen for you'll
    be shamed to disgrace.

You can always count on children to
    say, "No, it does not!"
And you'll end up embarrassed and
    flushing red-hot.

Have you discussed a thing of
   importance with your spouse last
   night?
Repeat it slightly off and your child will
   surely shed the light.

Parents, do heed my admonition,
That is, if you value your reputation.

Say nothing before your child that can
   be misconstrued in a young mind,
Or your child will publicly call you a
   liar and put you in a bind.

You can't blame children for you've
   taught them well,
That honesty is what they should
   practice, and the truth always tell.

The Terrible Threes

All that you've heard about *Terrible
    Threes* is no myth, though perhaps
    a slight exaggeration,
Parents, hold on to your hats and grit
    your teeth for the duration.

Coming out of infancy and into
    toddlerhood,
Is enough to throw anyone into a very
    confused mood.

The world isn't clear and never well
    defined,
All needs to be studied, explored and
    outlined.

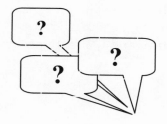

Asking "why?" is the three-year-old's
   never tiring attraction,
"Why this?" and "why that?"' enough
   to drive to distraction.

Another annoyance is the three-year-
   old's forte and calling,
All your requests get a "no!" while he
   continues stalling.

Many moons will pass before you,
   parents, can bet,
On your three-year-old to turn four
   and well-deserved rest to get.

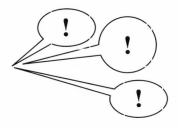

It'll happen when he grows out of those
    Terrible Threes,
From this impossible period you'll
    finally become divorcees.

You acquired a few more grey hairs to
    show for your trouble,
But believe me, as the three-year-old
    grows so will your distress double.

Sit back and enjoy the *Terrible Threes*
    all that you are able,
For this time of your lives may, after
    all, prove most tolerable.

Each age in your child's life is
    hampered with ups and downs,
So get smart, keep positive and please
    lose those frowns.

Wrong Tree

You're *barking up the wrong tree* when
   you expect,
Your teens to perceive messes with any
   respect.
Their rooms are cluttered with dirty
   clothing, remains of food and dead
   toads,
They look awful, smell badly and are
   seemingly unfit for human abodes.

Moms and Dads argue, "This is worse
   than a sty,"
But teens want to know, "Why?"
Moms are glared at while Dads get
   blank stares,
Thus provoking parental extraction
   of hairs.

Teens are obviously at ease where
    disorder looms,
Where sounds are loud and reeking
    with fumes.
Moms and Dads won't like what's
    there to see,
So they should stay away and let it
    all be.

Freddy's Arm

Freddy was only two years of age,
But his recklessness caused me
   great rage.
He endlessly put his young life
   on the line,
With actions I couldn't confine.

Worried and fearfully dreading,
I watched young Freddy toward
   danger treading.
With a hopeful prayer, nearly every
   day,
I rushed to move him out of harm's
   way.

Hearken to what Freddy did on
    an outing one bright afternoon,
You'd appreciate that my distress
    wasn't a mere motherly swoon.
From his stroller, Freddy reached
    to a horse we stopped to admire,
Straining and stretching higher and
    higher.

Freddy's arm soon disappeared out
    of sight,
From fingertips to shoulder's height.
It took me but a moment to realize
    the fact,
The horse had his arm but I couldn't
    act.

I stood there looking at my child
    and the horse,
Envisioning catastrophe or even
    worse.
But Freddy was pleased as can be,
Even the horse seemed to be smiling
    at me.

Not to startle the horse to do as
    I feared,
I froze in my spot while my eyes
    teared.
My own clammy forehead I shakily
    mopped,
Anxiously awaiting till this
    encounter stopped.

A Fallen Leaf

Parents view children as egocentric,
Because their demands make them
    frantic.
Certainly at times this conviction is
    true,
But at others it's faulty in every shade
    and hue.

Children are sentimental about things
    adults don't understand,
Such as preserving a fallen leaf close
    at hand.
Shedding tears while placing it betwixt
    pages of a favored book,
Is this child egotistic? Adults, please
    take a second or a third look!

There is no self-centeredness when
    one loves things outside oneself,
Selfless is he who holds deep feelings
    for a mere leaf kept in a book upon
    a shelf.
Charitable is one who cares for the
    weak and helpless,
Children possess these qualities,
    obscure but ever relentless.

Communication

Communication is the basis for all
    relationships,
Be it in the animal kingdom or in
    human fellowships.

Birds, dogs, cats and even dingoes,
Talk to their kind in their own unique
    lingoes.

Children are great at speaking with
    each other,
Being of different origins is never a
    bother.

They still possess that crucially
    important instinct,
Interaction for them hasn't yet become
    extinct.

Oral phrases aren't solely relied upon,
Because words can't always be
depended on.

Children still practice what grown-ups
have long forgotten,
With expressive gestures
communication can be gotten.

They intuitively know that body
language is an excellent tool,
For transmitting information at home,
in playgrounds and at school.

Feelings and ideas can easily be shared,
Hands and face for that purpose aren't
  spared.

In summation, please understand what
  I'm trying to say,
Words are important but our bodies a
  greater role should play.

Zipper Chin

Active child, filled with zeal,
Each transaction monumentally
    real.

Dance and gymnastics tackles with
    skill,
All approached with desire and will.

One day Stacy, for that is her name,
To please the coach was her special
    aim.

A challenging stunt attempted with
    resolution,
Fell and caused a serious contusion.

Wishing her hands to guard,
On her face she landed hard.

Chin hit the wooden floor with
  a bang,
Flesh ripped open with a pang.

To the hospital Stacy was rushed,
As wound gaped wide and blood
  gushed.

Doctor said it wasn't critical,
But chin required stitching and
  some topical.

Stacy was taken home with a
  beardlike bandage,
To cover her painfully wounded
  appendage.

To make a short story even shorter,
To the hospital twice more I was
   Stacy's escorter.

Twice within the next ten days,
Re-stitching was required on Stacy's
   face.

She just could not coordinate a fall,
A disastrous plunge didn't know
   how to stall.

Had Stacy's chin been equipped
   with a zipper,
Opening and closing would be
   painlessly quicker.

Boys and Girls

Humanity assents and thus decrees,
"Boys and girls are made of different
    things!"
But to explain where they came from
    has not been agreed on,
Nor has it ever been universally
    concurred upon.

Most young children, believe it or not,
Don't truthfully know how they were
    begot.
One story tells that they grew in a
    cabbage patch,
And there awaited parents to catch.

Another fable says that they were
  dropped through the chimney by
  a stork,
The same one delivering in Hong Kong
  and New York.
Still another silly myth states that they
  were purchased at a swap meet,
As each was displayed in a cute little
  seat.

I'm certain there are more tales out
  there,
Some amusing while others may
  perhaps scare.
As long as facts are not forthrightly
  told,
Fictitious stories will continually take
  hold.

The Teenager

Straight out of childhood and into this
    interim phase,
Not here nor there but in the limbo of
    space.
Too old for this yet too young for that,
Mood swings and outbursts at the drop
    of a hat.

Such are the afflictions of the teenager,
Even to himself he's an unwelcome
    stranger.
Those who must interact with this half
    ripened person,
Encounter mixed emotions for no
    apparent reason.

It's dreadfully hard to contend with
    these teen years,
Pervaded with anger, futility and tears.
My heart aches for those tormented by
    teenagitis and it makes me blue,
But I once had it myself and lived to
    tell about it, and so will you.

The truth and reality is that every
    person of age,
Had to go through this period of painful
    rage.
This is just one of the many facts of life,
Though seemingly pointless to put up
    with such strife.

I wish there was a smoother transition,
But such isn't the fact or tradition.
The bridge between childhood and
    maturity is rough and ragged,
You'll make it, though at times you'll
    have tripped and staggered.

It may not seem so right now, and at
    this point in time,
As stormy as they are, teenage years
    are your life's very prime.
This is when your personality is most
    dramatically contoured,
Where your life's course is routed and
    detoured.

Bravely encounter each incident,
Make it a positive learning event.
You could complain, groan and moan,
But for a second turn there is no loan.

This is the one and only chance you'll
    get,
So make it a good mold in which your
    life to set.
Teens are with you for a duration and
    will station you on insanity's brink,
But be assured that in retrospect those
    years seem as if passed in a blink.

Guardians of Peace

I implore and beseech, children out
    there,
Those living just about everywhere.
You still possess the knack to make
    peace,
On grace you haven't lost the lease.

You carry a talent deep in your heart,
From which adults have come apart.
I know not when they've lost their skill,
To make peace they no longer have
    the will.

I appoint you, children, to be guardians
    of peace,
"Forgive and forget" you master with
    ease.
You rarely harbor grudges,
'Cause you are such fair judges.

So, guard and protect this thing called
    peace,
Its security you must never tease.
Always and forever hold peace high,
Never ever let it die.

Suffering Teens

What saddens me greatly when meeting
    with teens,
Is their negative outlook on life and its
    scenes.

Invisible lenses seem to ride on their
    noses,
Through which they view the world and
    its many poses.

These lenses are obviously dark and
    graying,
Tainting all morbid and decaying.

I propose we exchange them for a rosier
    hue,
But I need some assistance from all
    of you.

Let's splash the universe in pastel
    pinks, blues and greens,
To make this planet livelier for those
    suffering teens.

Don't Toy with Your Food

"Don't toy with your food," I plea,
Attempting repeatedly to feed Bea.
Inventive and well endowed with
    imagination,
All are playthings without
    discrimination.

A napkin folded many times over,
Becomes a flying rover.
Knives and forks are Bea's weapons
    of valor,
Peas and beans are bullets to combat
    pallor.

Spoons, large and small, are perfect
   tools for digging,
Mashed potatoes and rice need
   rearranging and rigging.
Bright beyond her age, is my little Bea,
Alphabet in her cereal makes for a
   spelling-bee.

Sugar is snow on grapefruit, otherwise
   sour,
Its hollowed rind, like a cap, atop Bea's
   head will tower.
A bowl full of soup is a tiny ocean where
   vessels sail,
Breadcrumbs are ships caught in Bea's
   gale.

Spaghetti is serpents and Bea a dragon
   of evil temper,
Long creatures are inhaled in a
   scamper.
Ketchup is blood oozing from Bea's
   uninjured arteries,
UFOs are created from cubed carrots
   and celeries.

Once again I ask Bea to stop playing
   with her food,
It affects her not, nor does it change
   her mood.
I'm clearly mistaken when believing I'll
   succeed,
For Bea's games won't ever cease nor
   even recede.